Levels 4-6

Level Up MATHS

HOMEWORK BOOK

Author team: Greg and Lynn Byrd

LiveText

Heinemann

Heinemann is an imprint of Pearson Education Limited, a company incorporated in England and Wales, having its registered office at Edinburgh Gate, Harlow, Essex, CM20 2JE. Registered company number: 872828

www.heinemann.co.uk

Heinemann is a registered trademark of Pearson Education Limited

Text © Pearson Education Limited 2008

First published 2008

13
10 9 8 7

British Library Cataloguing in Publication Data is available from the British Library on request.

ISBN 978 0 435537 39 5

Copyright notice
All rights reserved. No part of this publication may be reproduced in any form or by any means (including photocopying or storing it in any medium by electronic means and whether or not transiently or incidentally to some other use of this publication) without the written permission of the copyright owner, except in accordance with the provisions of the Copyright, Designs and Patents Act 1988 or under the terms of a licence issued by the Copyright Licensing Agency, Saffron House, 6–10 Kirby Street, London ECIN 8TS (www.cla.co.uk). Applications for the copyright owner's written permission should be addressed to the publisher.

Edited by Maggie Rumble and Anne Packer
Designed by Pearson Education Ltd
Typeset by Tech-Set Ltd
Produced by Tech-Set Ltd
Original illustrations © Pearson Education Limited 2008
Illustrated by Beehive and Tech-Set Ltd
Cover design by Tom Cole (Seamonster Design)
Cover illustration by Max Ellis
Printed in China (CTPS/07)

Acknowledgements

The author and publisher would like to thank the following individuals and organisations for permission to reproduce photographs:

p6 © Shutterstock / Gladkova Svetlana; p6 © Shutterstock / Eric Isselee; p16 © Digital Vision; p21 © Shutterstock / Rainbow; p23 © Pearson Education Ltd / Tudor Photography; p33 © Shutterstock / Jaren Jai Wicklund; p37 © Shutterstock / Rebecca Abell; p60 © Pearson Education Ltd / Jules Selmes; p62 © Shutterstock / AlphaSpirit; p75 © Shutterstock / Chad McDermott; p84 © Shutterstock / Jason Bennee; p87 © Getty Images / Taxi

Every effort has been made to contact copyright holders of material reproduced in this book. Any omissions will be rectified in subsequent printings if notice is given to the publishers.

Contents

Welcome to Level Up Maths!

Level Up Maths is an inspirational new course for today's classroom. With stunning textbooks and amazing software, Key Stage 3 Maths has simply never looked this good!

The Homework Book has 18 units, with one homework page for each lesson in the Level Up 4–6 Textbook. The homework questions cover the same topics as the textbook pages, at the same levels.

> This shows where to look for help on the LiveText CD.

> Every homework starts with a question to practise your number skills.

> The sub-levelled questions practise the topics covered in the lesson.

> Your teacher may tell you to tick the questions to try.

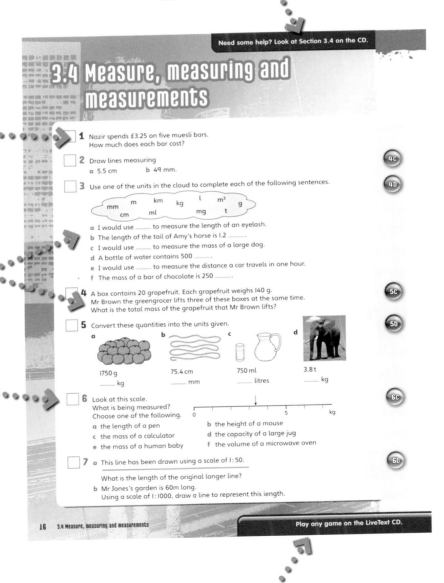

> This shows you the games to play on the LiveText CD. (Not for every homework.)

The LiveText CD

The LiveText CD in the back of this book has:

- The whole textbook on screen

Explanations, to help you understand the Big Ideas.

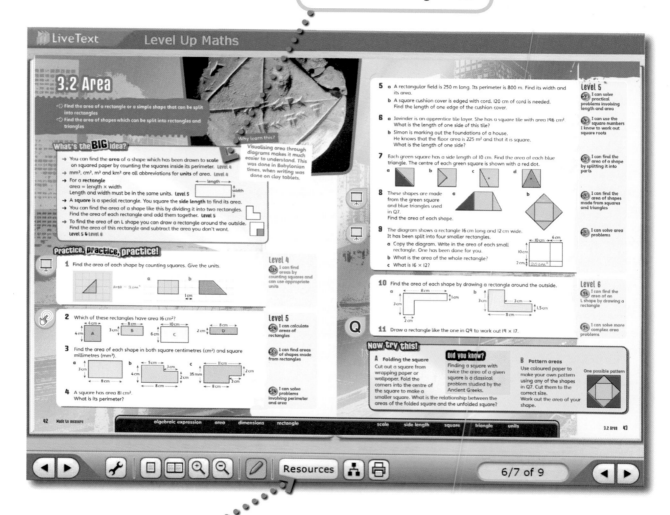

Glossary to explain maths words. Play audio to hear translations in Bengali, Gujarati, Punjabi, Turkish and Urdu.

- Games to practise your maths skills.

1.1 Sequences

1 Copy and complete this number pyramid.
Find each missing amount by
adding the two bricks below it.

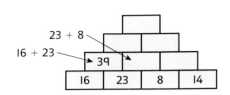

2 For each of these sequences, draw the next pattern in the sequence, and count how many dots are used in each of the patterns. Use this to check that the number of dots in your pattern is right.

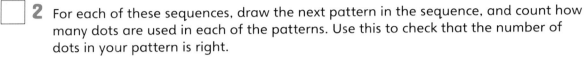

3 A computer is programmed to start at 5 and count on in steps of 3.

   a Write down the first four terms of this sequence.

   b Describe the term-to-term rule.

   c Is the sequence ascending or descending?

   d Is this sequence finite or infinite?

   e Find the 10th term in the sequence.

4 Write the first five terms of each of these sequences.

   a first term 4, term-to-term rule ×3 +1   **b** first term 3, term-to-term rule ×4 +1

   c first term 1, term-to-term rule ×3 +4   **d** first term 1, term-to-term rule ×4 +3

5 Clive's laser printer has smudged when printing his homework.
Copy Clive's homework and fill in the smudged terms for him.

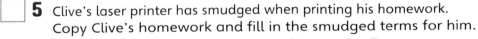

6 Clive's laser printer has smudged even more on this question.
Copy his answers and fill in the smudged parts for him.

   a 1, 5, ⬤, ⬤, ⬤,   term⬤term rule is ×3 −1

   b 2, 3, 6, ⬤, ⬤,   term to term⬤is ×3⬤

   c 20, 12, ⬤, ⬤, ⬤,   term to⬤rule is ÷2⬤

   d 80, 38, ⬤, ⬤, ⬤,   ⬤to term rule is ÷2⬤

7 Clive's last question has smudged the worst!
Copy out what you can read, and fill in possible answers for the smudged parts.

   a 1, ⬤, 7   term-to-term rule is ⬤   **b** 1, ⬤, 9   term-to⬤

   c 3, ⬤, 12   term ⬤   **d** 4, ⬤, 100⬤

1.2 Generating sequences

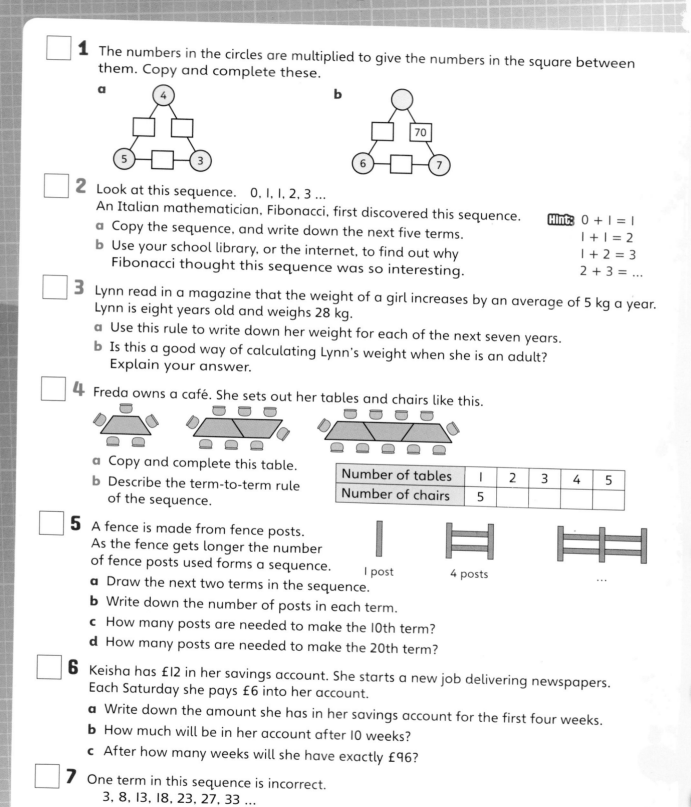

1 The numbers in the circles are multiplied to give the numbers in the square between them. Copy and complete these.

a

b

2 Look at this sequence. 0, 1, 1, 2, 3 ...
An Italian mathematician, Fibonacci, first discovered this sequence.

Hint: 0 + 1 = 1
1 + 1 = 2
1 + 2 = 3
2 + 3 = ...

a Copy the sequence, and write down the next five terms.
b Use your school library, or the internet, to find out why Fibonacci thought this sequence was so interesting.

3 Lynn read in a magazine that the weight of a girl increases by an average of 5 kg a year. Lynn is eight years old and weighs 28 kg.

a Use this rule to write down her weight for each of the next seven years.
b Is this a good way of calculating Lynn's weight when she is an adult? Explain your answer.

4 Freda owns a café. She sets out her tables and chairs like this.

a Copy and complete this table.
b Describe the term-to-term rule of the sequence.

Number of tables	1	2	3	4	5
Number of chairs	5				

5 A fence is made from fence posts. As the fence gets longer the number of fence posts used forms a sequence.

1 post

4 posts

...

a Draw the next two terms in the sequence.
b Write down the number of posts in each term.
c How many posts are needed to make the 10th term?
d How many posts are needed to make the 20th term?

6 Keisha has £12 in her savings account. She starts a new job delivering newspapers. Each Saturday she pays £6 into her account.

a Write down the amount she has in her savings account for the first four weeks.
b How much will be in her account after 10 weeks?
c After how many weeks will she have exactly £96?

7 One term in this sequence is incorrect.
3, 8, 13, 18, 23, 27, 33 ...

a Write down the correct sequence.
b Write down the value of the 20th term in the sequence.

4b

4a

4a

5c

5c

5c

1.3 More sequences

1 All of these fractions can be put into pairs of equivalent fractions, except one. Which one of these fractions has no equivalent partner?

$\frac{6}{16}$ $\frac{8}{12}$ $\frac{4}{5}$ $\frac{3}{4}$ $\frac{8}{10}$ $\frac{3}{8}$ $\frac{12}{16}$ $\frac{8}{16}$ $\frac{2}{3}$

2 Copy and complete this sequence that shows powers of 10.

a

10^1	10^2	10^3	10^4	10^5
10	10×10	$10 \times 10 \times 10$	_____	_____
10	100	_____	_____	_____

b Describe the term-to-term rule.

3 Look at this sequence.

2, 5, 7, 10, 12, 15, ...

Explain why this is **not** an arithmetic sequence.

4 This sequence of shapes is made from yellow tiles and blue tiles.

Shape 1
2 yellow tiles
2 blue tiles

Shape 2
3 yellow tiles
4 blue tiles

Shape 3
_____
_____

a Draw the next two shapes in the sequence.

b Copy and complete this table, showing number of yellow tiles and number of blue tiles.

Shape number	1	2	3	4	5
yellow tiles	2	3			
blue tiles	2	4			

c Write down any patterns you notice about the yellow tiles and the blue tiles.

d Write in your own words the term-to-term rules for the yellow and blue tiles.

e Copy and complete these sentences to describe the position-to-term rules.
   i number of yellow tiles = shape number + ____
   ii number of blue tiles = shape number × ____

f Use your position-to-term rules to find the number of yellow tiles and the number of blue tiles in the 10th term in the sequence.

5 Write the first five terms of the sequence with position-to-term rule (2 × position number) + 10.

6 Describe in words the term-to-term rule for the sequence with position-to-term rule (2 × position number) + 10.

7 Explain the connection between the term-to-term rule and the position-to-term rule for the sequence (2 × position number) + 10.

1.4 Function machines

1 These prices are displayed in a shop window.
Write the prices in order, starting with the cheapest.

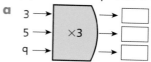

85p   £1.25   £0.69   £0.12   150p

2 Copy and complete these function machines.

a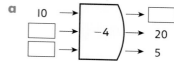

b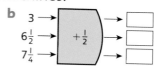

3 Copy and complete these function machines.

a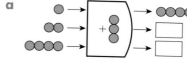

b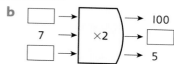

4 Copy and complete these function machines.

a

b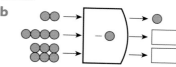

5 Copy and complete these function machines.

a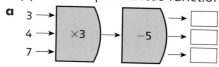

b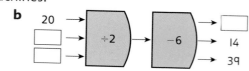

6 Write function machines to solve these problems then answer the questions.

a I think of a number, multiply by 2 then add 20.
The answer is 32. What was the number that I thought of?

b I think of a number, add 2 then multiply by 2.
The answer is 18. What was the number that I thought of?

c I think of a number, double it, then double it again.
The answer is 32. What was the number that I thought of?

7 Find the function for these sets of inputs and outputs.

a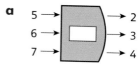

b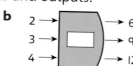

c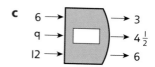

d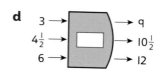

1.5 Expressions and mappings

1 The numbers in the circles are multiplied together to give the numbers in the square between them.
Copy and complete these.

a
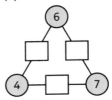

b
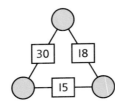

2 Work out the value of these expressions.

a $3 + 4 \times 5$ **b** $(8 + 4) \div 3$ **c** $(17 - 7)^2$ **d** $(9 + 11) \times 3$

3 Simplify these expressions.

a $g + g + g + g$ **b** $4f + 6f$

c $9p - 2p$ **d** $6t + t - 4t$

4 These cards show algebraic expressions.
The blue cards are unsimplified and the red cards are simplified.
Match each blue card to the correct red card.

$a + 2a + a$ $8a + 2a - 5a$ $4a$ $a + 4a - 2a$ $5a$

$6a$ $3a$ $7a - 2a + a$

5 Simplify these expressions.

a $4h + 8 - 2h + 6$ **b** $5u + 3v + 2u - v$ **c** $3x + 4y + 6 - 2 + 5x - y$

d $4 \times 6k$ **e** $15j \div 3$ **f** $\frac{1}{4} \times 16p$

6 Draw mapping diagrams to represent these functions.
For both questions, draw a pair of number lines from 0 to 10.

a $x \longrightarrow x + 7$ **b** $x \longrightarrow 2x$

7 Write an algebraic mapping to describe these sets of inputs and outputs.

a $7 \longrightarrow 2$ **b** $0 \longrightarrow 0$ **c** $0 \longrightarrow 0$
     $3 \longrightarrow -2$ $-2 \longrightarrow -4$ $-2 \longrightarrow -1$
     $5 \longrightarrow 0$ $5 \longrightarrow 10$ $5 \longrightarrow 2\frac{1}{2}$
     $-9 \longrightarrow -14$ $1 \longrightarrow 2$ $1 \longrightarrow 0.5$

5c   5c   5c   5b   6c   6c

Play any game on the LiveText CD.

1.6 Constructing expressions

1 Copy this multiplication grid.
Complete the grid as quickly as you can.
Use a stopwatch to time how long it takes you.

×	3	6	2	8	5	4	9
4							
6							
8							
7							
3							
5							
2							

2 Write expressions for
  a 6 less than a **b** b less than 8
  c double c **d** half of d

3 Jake has j coins in his pocket, Kris has k coins in his pocket and Mikka has m coins in her pocket.
Write expressions for the number of coins in:
  a Jake's pocket after he has taken out three coins
  b Mikka's pocket after she has put in three coins
  c Jake's pocket after he has been given all of Kris's coins.

4 Monica's cat weighs x kg and her dog weighs y kg.
Write expressions for animals that are:
  a three times heavier than her cat
  b twice as heavy as her dog
  c p multiplied by her dog's weight
  d as heavy as the sum of her cat's weight and her dog's weight.

5 Ross has five cats. Each cat weighs c kg.
He also has three dogs. Each dog weighs d kg.
Write expressions for the total weight of:
  a all five cats
  b two of the dogs
  c two of the cats and two of the dogs
  d four of the cats and one of the dogs who is wearing a coat weighing $\frac{1}{2}$ kg.

6 Imagine two mystery numbers p and q.
Construct expressions for:
  a 2 more than 10 times p
  b a quarter of q
  c p multiplied by itself then add q
  d 100 divided by q.

p q

7 A mystery amount of money is m.
Write expressions for these amounts:
  a three times as large as the mystery number
  b the amount shared equally between four people
  c the amount squared
  d double the amount of money and then squared.

£m

Play any game on the LiveText CD.

2.1 Decimal know-how

1 Look at the table below.
The column on the left has numbers written in words.
The column on the right has numbers written in figures.
Match each number on the left with the correct number on the right.
The first one has been done for you.

	Number in words
A	two thousand four hundred
B	twenty thousand and forty
C	two hundred thousand and four
D	two thousand and forty four
E	twenty four thousand four hundred
F	two hundred thousand and forty

	Number in figures
G	200 004
H	2 044
I	2 400
J	24 400
K	200 040
L	20 040

A matches with I

2 Write the value, in words, of the seven in each of these numbers.

  a 37.665   **b** 14.976   **c** 3.708   **d** 21.007

3 Put these tins of paint in order of size starting with the smallest.

45 cl   1.25 l   300 ml   0.38 l   150 cl   750 ml

4 Write **true** or **false** for each of the following statements.

  a $3.2 \times 10 = 0.32$ **b** $4.25 \times 100 = 425$ **c** $60.5 \div 1000 = 0.605$

  d $476 \div 100 = 4.76$ **e** $0.0558 \times 1000 = 55.8$ **f** $0.25 \div 10 = 2.5$

5 Copy and complete the following statements.

  a $2.5 \times 10 = \boxed{}$ **b** $0.562 \times \boxed{} = 562$ **c** $\boxed{} \times 100 = 43.5$

  d $4.7 \div \boxed{} = 0.47$ **e** $\boxed{} \div 100 = 0.665$ **f** $45.5 \div 1000 = \boxed{}$

6 Arrange these cards in descending order.

3.414   3.219   3.5   3.236   3.48

7 a Arrange these cards in ascending order.

0.424	0.415	0.4682	0.4239	0.4236	0.4681	0.41
M	E	L	I	C	A	D

  b What word have you written?

Need some help? Look at Section 2.2 on the CD.

2.2 Negative numbers

1 **a** Copy this secret code box.

										Y	!
43	3200	20	90	430		900	430		200	3200	430	320

b Work out the answers to these questions.
Put the letter by each question on the line
above the answer in the secret code box.
The first one is done for you.
What is the secret message?

32 × 10 = Y	200 ÷ 10 = T
9 × 100 = I	43000 ÷ 100 = S
430 ÷ 10 = M	20 × 10 = E
9000 ÷ 100 = H	32 × 100 = A

2 Put these temperatures in order, coldest first.

a 4°C, −2°C, 3°C, −5°C, 0°C   **b** −7°C, 8°C, 4°C, −9°C, 1°C, −11°C

3 What is the new temperature for examples **b** to **e**?
Example **a** is done for you.

	Old temperature	Change in temperature	New temperature
a	3°C	5°C colder	−2°C
b	−2°C	3°C warmer	
c	−1°C	4°C colder	
d	6°C	5°C colder	
e	−9°C	6°C warmer	

4 In this number wheel
opposite numbers add up to −15.
Copy the wheel and fill in the
missing numbers.

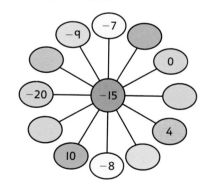

5 Copy and complete the following.

a −2 × 4 = ☐   **b** 6 × −5 = ☐   **c** 2 × −10= ☐   **d** −9 × 0 = ☐

e 12 ÷ −6 = ☐   **f** −16 ÷ 4 = ☐   **g** 8 ÷ −8 = ☐   **h** −21 ÷ 7 = ☐

6 Copy and complete the following.

a −3 × −5 = ☐   **b** ☐ × −6 = 24   **c** −2 × ☐ = −20   **d** 8 × 4 = ☐

e 18 ÷ ☐ = −9   **f** −28 ÷ ☐ = 7   **g** −6 ÷ 6 = ☐   **h** ☐ ÷ −8 = 5

7 Arrange these cards in ascending order.

−3.42   −4.1   −3.48   −4.6   −3.15   −4.05

2.3 Addition and subtraction

1 This is a MCC (Mental Challenge Curve). Copy the curve.
Start at the first calculation, then in your head work out the missing values.

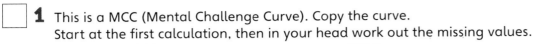
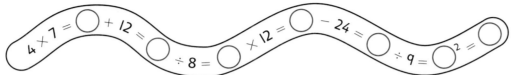

2 In this diagram, opposite numbers add to 100.
Copy and complete the diagram.
The first one has been done for you.

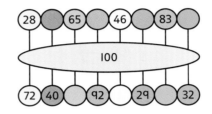

3 Lynn is buying food for her dog.
She buys a bag of dog meal for £2.49,
tinned food for £1.86 and some treats for £1.35.

   a How much does she spend in total?

   b She pays with a £10 note.
      How much change does she receive?

4 Use the column method to work out these additions.
Use an estimate to check your answer.

   a 476 + 295 + 53   **b** 2.56 + 45.09 + 112.7   **c** 24.6 + 9.96 + 72

5 Work out the following subtractions.

   a 493 − 359   **b** 14 664 − 8 278   **c** 35.28 − 14.36   **d** 8.4 − 3.87

6 Copy and complete this number pyramid.
Find each missing number by adding
the two bricks below it.

7 Copy and complete this number pyramid.
Each brick is the sum of the two bricks below it.

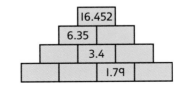

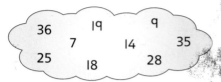

2.4 Multiplication

1 Use the numbers in the cloud to complete these additions.
You can use each number in the cloud once only.

a $12 + 23 = \boxed{}$ b $\boxed{} + 13 = 41$

c $17 + \boxed{} = 36$ d $\boxed{} + \boxed{} = 39$

e $\boxed{} + \boxed{} = 27$ f $\boxed{} + 29 = \boxed{}$

Cloud numbers: 36   19   9   7   14   35   25   18   28

2 Copy and complete these multiplications.
Use the grid method in parts **a** and **b**. Use the standard method in parts **c** and **d**.

a 243×7

×	200	40	3
7			

b 359×6

×	300	50	9
6			

c 724×5

```
    7 2 4
  ×     5
  _____
```

d 187×8

```
    1 8 7
  ×     8
  _____
```

3 In the shape below, the numbers in the two circles multiply together to give the number in the square between them. Copy and complete.

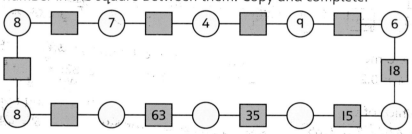

4 Use a mental method to work these out.

a 4×0.2 b 7×0.8 c 0.03×3 d 0.09×5

5 Which of these are correct? Check each calculation by working backwards.

a $473 \times 5 = 2365$ b $369 \times 4 = 1467$ c $821 \times 6 = 4926$

6 Work out these multiplications.
Use the grid method in parts **a** and **b**. Use the standard method in parts **c** and **d**.

a 23×42 b 60×18 c 54×93 d 78×26

7 Ceri is buying insurance for her horse.
She sees this advert in a magazine.

Work out the total amount that Ceri
has to pay for

a Option A

b Option B

c Option C

> **'Old Nag' Horse Insurance**
>
> *Option A:* £23 per month for 12 months
> *Option B:* £21 per month for 18 months
> *Option C:* £17 per month for 24 months

2.5 Squares and square roots

1 Mary is saving for an MP3 player that costs £80. She has saved £55.
She does a calculation on her calculator and gets an answer of −25.

   a What calculation has she done?

   b Explain what −25 means.

2 **a** Which of the numbers on the cards below are square numbers?

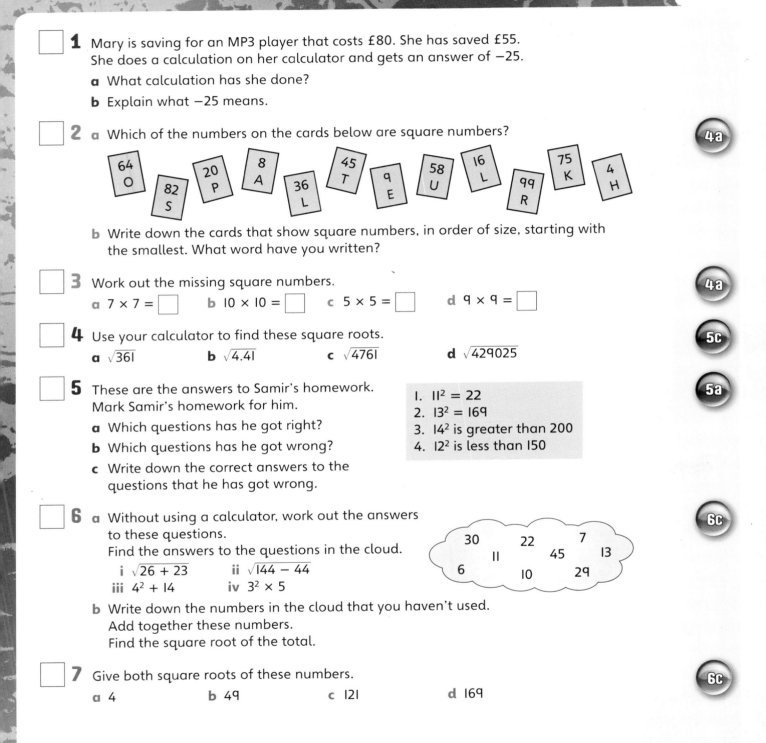

   b Write down the cards that show square numbers, in order of size, starting with
the smallest. What word have you written?

3 Work out the missing square numbers.

   a $7 \times 7 = \square$ **b** $10 \times 10 = \square$ **c** $5 \times 5 = \square$ **d** $9 \times 9 = \square$

4 Use your calculator to find these square roots.

   a $\sqrt{361}$ **b** $\sqrt{4.41}$ **c** $\sqrt{4761}$ **d** $\sqrt{429025}$

5 These are the answers to Samir's homework.
Mark Samir's homework for him.

   a Which questions has he got right?

   b Which questions has he got wrong?

   c Write down the correct answers to the
questions that he has got wrong.

> 1. $11^2 = 22$
> 2. $13^2 = 169$
> 3. 14^2 is greater than 200
> 4. 12^2 is less than 150

6 **a** Without using a calculator, work out the answers
to these questions.
Find the answers to the questions in the cloud.

      i $\sqrt{26 + 23}$ **ii** $\sqrt{144 - 44}$

     iii $4^2 + 14$ **iv** $3^2 \times 5$

Cloud: 30   22   7   11   45   13   6   10   29

   b Write down the numbers in the cloud that you haven't used.
Add together these numbers.
Find the square root of the total.

7 Give both square roots of these numbers.

   a 4   **b** 49   **c** 121   **d** 169

Side markers: 4a, 4a, 5c, 5a, 6c, 6c

2.6 Division

1 The numbers in the circles are added together to give the numbers in the squares.
Copy and complete these.

a
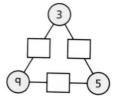

b
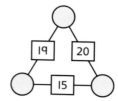

2 Work out these exact divisions.

  a 936 ÷ 3   **b** 208 ÷ 4   **c** 905 ÷ 5   **d** 258 ÷ 6

3 Copy and complete the following.

  a 14 × 12 = 168   168 ÷ 14 = ☐   ☐ ÷ 12 = 14

  b 27 × 25 = 675   ☐ ÷ 25 = 27   675 ÷ ☐ = 25

  c 576 ÷ 18 = ☐   576 ÷ 32 = ☐   18 × 32 = 576

4 Which of these are correct? Check each calculation by working backwards.

  a 47 × 5 = 235   **b** 421 × 6 = 5226   **c** 784 × 3 = 2342

5 Work out these exact divisions.

  a 187 ÷ 11   **b** 576 ÷ 16   **c** 825 ÷ 25

6 Work out these divisions. Write the remainders as fractions.

  a 437 ÷ 12   **b** 791 ÷ 23   **c** 1427 ÷ 31

7 Megan wants to buy a new car.
She sees the same car for sale in two different garages.

> ≡**CARS 'R' US**
>
> **PRICE: £7980**
> **PAYMENT METHOD:**
> **Equal monthly**
> **payments over**
> **12 months**

> **Mo's Motors**
>
> **PRICE: £7500**
> **PAYMENT METHOD:**
> **Deposit of £1200**
> **then equal monthly**
> **payments of the**
> **remaining amount**
> **over 18 months**

Work out the monthly payments if Megan buys the car from

a Cars 'R' Us

b Mo's Motors.

4b
4a
4a
5b
5b
5b

Play any game on the LiveTex CD

3.1 Perimeter

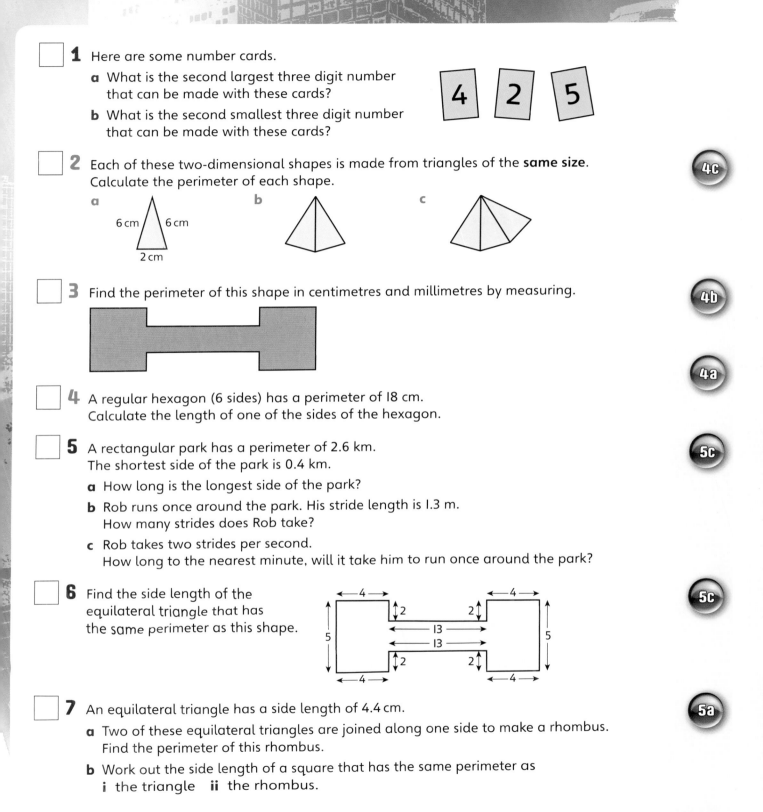

1 Here are some number cards.

   a What is the second largest three digit number that can be made with these cards?

   b What is the second smallest three digit number that can be made with these cards?

2 Each of these two-dimensional shapes is made from triangles of the **same size**. Calculate the perimeter of each shape.

   a   6 cm 6 cm   2 cm   **b**   **c**

3 Find the perimeter of this shape in centimetres and millimetres by measuring.

4 A regular hexagon (6 sides) has a perimeter of 18 cm.
   Calculate the length of one of the sides of the hexagon.

5 A rectangular park has a perimeter of 2.6 km.
   The shortest side of the park is 0.4 km.

   a How long is the longest side of the park?

   b Rob runs once around the park. His stride length is 1.3 m.
      How many strides does Rob take?

   c Rob takes two strides per second.
      How long to the nearest minute, will it take him to run once around the park?

6 Find the side length of the equilateral triangle that has the same perimeter as this shape.

7 An equilateral triangle has a side length of 4.4 cm.

   a Two of these equilateral triangles are joined along one side to make a rhombus.
      Find the perimeter of this rhombus.

   b Work out the side length of a square that has the same perimeter as
      i the triangle **ii** the rhombus.

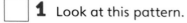

3.2 Area

1 Look at this pattern.

D	O	G	D	O	G	D	O	G	...
1	2	3	4	5	6	7	8	9	...

When the pattern is continued, the letter D will be above the number 10.

a Which letter will be above the number 15?

b Which letter will be above the number 62?

c Which number will be below the 10th G?

2 Find the area of this shape by counting squares.

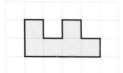

3 Find the area of this shape.

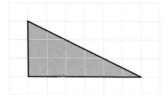

4 Find the area of this shape.

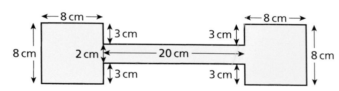

5 The state of Wyoming (in America) is rectangular in shape. The length is 360 miles. The perimeter is 1 264 miles. What is **a** the width **b** the area of Wyoming?

6 Find the area of this shape.

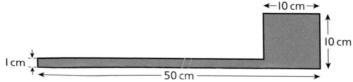

7 Fred is building a pen for his goats. He has 24 fence panels, each measuring 1 m.
He wants to build a rectanguar pen with the largest area possible
This is Fred's first attempt.

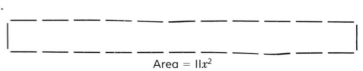

Area = $11x^2$

a How can Fred arrange the 24 fence panels to get the rectangle with the largest area? Draw a diagram.

b What is the largest area?

3.3 Areas of triangles, parallelograms and trapeziums

1 The pupils in a class arranged themselves into pairs. There was one pupil left over.
They then arranged themselves into groups of three. There was one pupil left over.
They then arranged themselves into groups of five. No one was left over.
How many pupils are in the class? **Hint:** There are fewer than 50.

2 Each of these parallelograms is cut up and rearranged to make a rectangle.
Match each of the parallelograms with its correct rectangle.

3 Each of these triangles is cut up and rearranged to make a rectangle.
Match each of the triangles with its correct rectangle.

4 By cutting the square along the dotted line
and joining shape A to shape B,
two other quadrilaterals can be made.
Name the two shapes and draw them accurately.

5 Find the area of this triangle.

6 Find the area of this parallelogram.

7 Find the area of this trapezium.

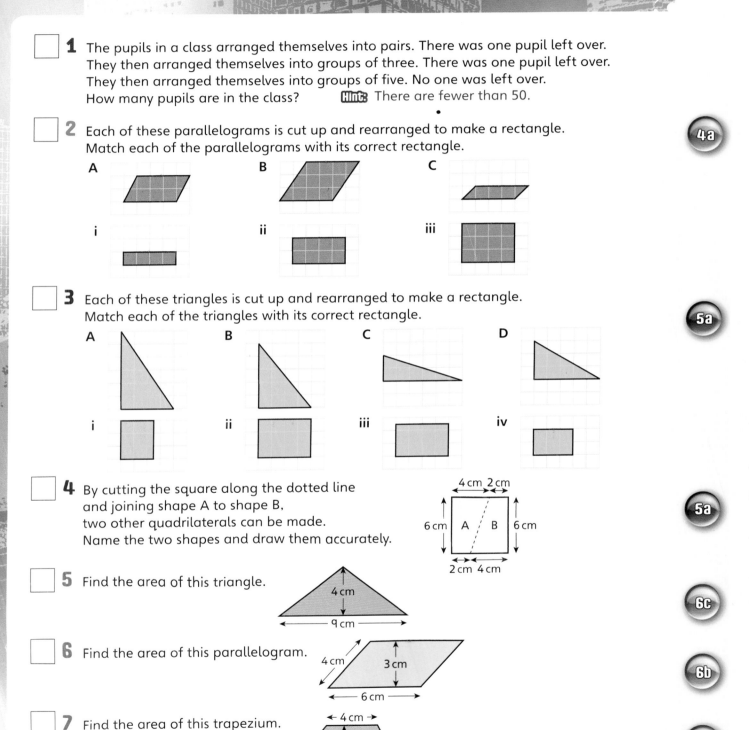

ny game on the LiveText CD.

3.4 Measure, measuring and measurements

1 Nazir spends £3.25 on five muesli bars.
How much does each bar cost?

2 Draw lines measuring
  a 5.5 cm   **b** 49 mm.

3 Use one of the units in the cloud to complete each of the following sentences.

> mm   m   km   kg   l   m³   g
> cm   ml   mg   t

  a I would use _____ to measure the length of an eyelash.
  b The length of the tail of Amy's horse is 1.2 _____.
  c I would use _____ to measure the mass of a large dog.
  d A bottle of water contains 500 _____.
  e I would use _____ to measure the distance a car travels in one hour.
  f The mass of a bar of chocolate is 250 _____.

4 A box contains 20 grapefruit. Each grapefruit weighs 140 g.
Mr Brown the greengrocer lifts three of these boxes at the same time.
What is the total mass of the grapefruit that Mr Brown lifts?

5 Convert these quantities into the units given.

  a   **b**   **c**   **d**

  1750 g   75.4 cm   750 ml   3.8 t
  _____ kg   _____ mm   _____ litres   _____ kg

6 Look at this scale.
What is being measured?
Choose one of the following.

  0 _____ 5 _____ kg

  a the length of a pen   **b** the height of a mouse
  c the mass of a calculator   **d** the capacity of a large jug
  e the mass of a human baby   **f** the volume of a microwave oven

7 **a** This line has been drawn using a scale of 1:50.

  What is the length of the original longer line?

  b Mr Jones's garden is 60m long.
  Using a scale of 1:1000, draw a line to represent this length.

4c
4b
5c
5b
6c
6

Play any game on the Live

4.1 Fractions

1 Copy and complete this number puzzle.

5	×		=	20		
		×		÷		
6		4	×	2	=	8
×		=		=		×
				−		=
=						=
	÷	2	=	18		

2 What fraction of each circle is shaded?

a   b   c   d

3 All of these fractions can be put into pairs of equivalent fractions, except one. Which one of these fractions has no equivalent partner?

$\frac{8}{16}$ $\frac{2}{3}$ $\frac{4}{5}$ $\frac{1}{2}$ $\frac{20}{25}$ $\frac{5}{8}$ $\frac{10}{12}$ $\frac{3}{7}$ $\frac{14}{15}$ $\frac{15}{35}$ $\frac{10}{15}$ $\frac{5}{6}$ $\frac{28}{30}$

4 All of these fractions are equivalent to each other, except one. Which one of these fractions is not equivalent to the others?

$\frac{30}{70}$ $\frac{6}{14}$ $\frac{15}{35}$ $\frac{12}{21}$ $\frac{27}{63}$ $\frac{12}{28}$ **Hint:** Change all the fractions into sevenths.

5 Use a diagram to work out which of each pair of fractions is greater.

a $\frac{3}{4}$ or $\frac{5}{7}$ b $\frac{2}{5}$ or $\frac{3}{8}$ c $\frac{2}{3}$ or $\frac{4}{7}$

6 Write these fractions in their simplest form.

a $\frac{50}{70}$ b $\frac{18}{21}$ c $\frac{15}{40}$ d $\frac{32}{64}$

7 Convert these terminating decimals to fractions.

a 0.9   b 0.111   c 0.03   d 0.099

8 Convert these terminating decimals to fractions. Write each fraction in its simplest form.

a 0.8   b 0.112   c 0.04   d 0.100

4.2 Adding and subtracting fractions

1 Find the missing values from the table below.

	Town	Temperature at midday	Temperature at 6 p.m.	Fall in temperature
a	Kinross	6°C	1°C	
b	Kinel	−2°C	−7°C	
c	Kinurt	0°C		3°C
d	Kincold	3°C		4°C

2 Find the missing numbers to make these fractions equivalent.

$$\frac{\square}{15} = \frac{\square}{6} = \frac{2}{3} = \frac{12}{\square} = \frac{20}{\square}$$

3 Which of these shapes has the equivalent of $\frac{2}{5}$ shaded?

a   **b** 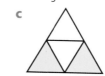   **c**   **d**

4 Phoebe ate $\frac{2}{5}$ of a pie. What fraction of the pie did she not eat?

5 Work out $\frac{5}{8} - \frac{3}{8} + \frac{2}{8} - \frac{1}{8}$

6 Faruq went to a pizza party. All the pizzas were 'Family size' pizzas.
The ham pizzas were cut into quarters.
The mushroom pizzas were cut into fifths.
Faruq ate one slice of ham pizza and one slice of mushroom pizza.
What fraction of a whole pizza did he eat altogether?

7 Bill had $\frac{5}{7}$ of a box of chocolates left. Jane ate $\frac{1}{2}$ of these.
What fraction of the box of chocolates has Bill now got left?

8 Work these out. If necessary, simplify your answer.

a $\frac{2}{3} + \frac{2}{9}$ **b** $\frac{1}{5} + \frac{3}{4}$ **c** $\frac{1}{4} + \frac{5}{12}$

9 In a magic square, all the rows, columns and
diagonals add up to the same number.
Copy and complete this magic square.

$\frac{3}{8}$		$\frac{1}{2}$
$\frac{7}{16}$		
$\frac{1}{8}$	$\frac{9}{16}$	

4.3 Improper fractions and mixed numbers

1 Put the numbers 1, 2, 3, 4, 5 and 6 into the circles so that the numbers on each side of the triangle add up to 9.

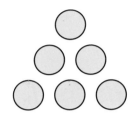

2 Use a mental method to work out
   a $\frac{3}{10} + \frac{2}{5}$ **b** $\frac{7}{10} - \frac{2}{5}$ **c** $\frac{2}{5} + \frac{2}{5} + \frac{2}{5}$

3 Each of these shapes represents $\frac{1}{4}$ of a pizza.

   a Write down the total amount of pizza as an improper fraction.
   b Write down the total amount of pizza as a mixed number.

4 Convert these improper fractions to mixed numbers.
   a $\frac{5}{3}$ **b** $\frac{12}{11}$ **c** $\frac{12}{5}$ **d** $\frac{5}{2}$

5 Add these mixed numbers.
   Write your answer as a mixed number in its simplest form.
   a $1\frac{3}{4} + 4\frac{3}{8}$ **b** $1\frac{3}{4} + 4\frac{3}{5}$

6 Do these subtractions.
   Write your answer as a mixed number in its simplest form.
   a $4\frac{3}{4} - 1\frac{3}{8}$ **b** $4\frac{3}{4} - 1\frac{3}{5}$

7 Do these subtractions. Show all your working.
   Write your answer as a mixed number in its simplest form.
   a $4\frac{3}{8} - 1\frac{3}{4}$ **b** $4\frac{3}{5} - 1\frac{3}{4}$

8 Evan has $6\frac{3}{4}$ litres of red paint and $2\frac{9}{10}$ litres of blue paint.
   How much more red paint than blue paint does he have?

4.4 Multiplying and dividing with fractions

1 Write **true** or **false** for each of these.

    a 10 is a factor of 5   **b** 5 is a factor of 10

    c 36 is a multiple of 6   **d** 6 is a multiple of 36

    e $72 \div 5$ has a remainder of 2   **f** $72 \div 4$ has a remainder of 3

    g 99 is a square number   **h** 4 is the square root of 16

2 Match each pink question card with the correct blue answer card.

A	B	C	D
$\frac{3}{4}$ of £24	$\frac{4}{5}$ of £30	$\frac{5}{8}$ of £32	$\frac{6}{7}$ of £14

i	ii	iii	iv
£24	£12	£18	£20

3 Work out whether **A**, **B**, or **C** is the correct answer for each of these.

    a $\frac{2}{5} \times 20 =$ **A** 4   **B** 12   **C** 8

    b $\frac{3}{7} \times 21 =$ **A** 9   **B** 3   **C** 49

    c $\frac{9}{10} \times 70 =$ **A** 7   **B** 36   **C** 63

4 Ian has a 40 g jar of chilli paste. He uses $\frac{5}{8}$ of the chilli paste. How many grams of the chilli paste has he used?

5 Work these out.
Give your answer as a mixed number where appropriate.

    a $16 \times \frac{3}{4}$ **b** $22 \times \frac{5}{6}$ **c** $13 \times \frac{3}{5}$

6 Copy and complete.

    a $8 \div \frac{1}{6} = 48$ $8 \div \frac{2}{6} = 24$ $8 \div \frac{3}{6} = \boxed{}$ $8 \div \frac{4}{6} = \boxed{}$

    b $12 \div \frac{1}{5} = 60$ $12 \div \frac{2}{5} = \boxed{}$ $12 \div \frac{3}{5} = \boxed{}$ $12 \div \frac{4}{5} = \boxed{}$

7 Choose the correct statement from the cloud to finish each of these sentences.

    gets bigger   gets smaller   stays the same

    a When I multiply a number by one, the number _____.

    b When I multiply a number by a fraction less than one, the number _____.

    c When I divide a number by a fraction less than one, the number _____.

4.5 Fractions, decimals and percentages

1 Eggs are packed in boxes of 6.
  a How many boxes are needed for 350 eggs?
  b How many **more** eggs are needed so that all the boxes are full?

2 What percentage of each shape is shaded?
  a
  b

3 Put these cards into groups of three equivalent cards.
Each group must contain one pink, one yellow and one blue card.

0.11   10%   37%   0.37   30%

$\frac{37}{100}$ $\frac{11}{100}$ $\frac{7}{100}$

$\frac{1}{10}$ $\frac{3}{10}$

7%   0.3   0.07   11%   0.1

4 a What is $\frac{1}{4}$ as a decimal?
  b Use your answer to part **a** to write $\frac{3}{4}$ as a decimal.
  c $\frac{1}{20}$ written as a decimal is 0.05.
     Use this fact to write $\frac{3}{20}$, $\frac{7}{20}$ and $\frac{11}{20}$ as decimals.

5 Convert these decimals to fractions in their simplest form.
  a 0.19   **b** 0.28   **c** 0.375   **d** 0.805

6 Convert these fractions to decimals using written division.
  a $\frac{9}{5}$ **b** $\frac{11}{4}$ **c** $\frac{5}{8}$ **d** $\frac{4}{9}$

7 Use equivalent fractions to put these fraction cards in order, starting with the smallest.
  a $\frac{1}{4}$ $\frac{3}{8}$ $\frac{3}{16}$
  b $\frac{13}{20}$ $\frac{1}{10}$ $\frac{3}{4}$ $\frac{2}{5}$

8 $\frac{1}{8}$ = 0.125. Work out the decimal equivalent of   **a** $\frac{1}{80}$ **b** $\frac{1}{40}$.

4c
4b
5a
5a
6c
6b
6a

Play any game on the LiveText CD.

4.6 Internet shop

1 Find the missing numbers to make these fractions equivalent.

$$\frac{\square}{16} = \frac{\square}{8} = \frac{3}{4} = \frac{9}{\square} = \frac{18}{\square}$$

2 In a pizza eating competition, competitors have 30 seconds to eat as much pizza as they can.
But their pizzas are different sizes!
This diagram shows the size of each pizza and the percentage that was eaten by a competitor.
Put the competitors in order, starting with the one who ate the most.

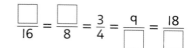

Giovanni 25% 1100 g
Leonardo 40% 750 g
Angelo 80% 400 g
Fredo 95% 300 g

3 Over the last year, three of the pizza eaters have put on weight and the other has lost weight. Match each statement on the left with the correct multiplier on the right.

Giovanni's weight increased by 2%

Leonardo's weight increased by 20%

Fredo's weight decreased by 10%

Angelo's weight increased by 10%

× 1.2
× 1.22
× 2
× 1.02
× 0.9
× 1.1
× 1.010

4 Giovanni is a pizza salesman. He is paid a 10% commission on every sale he makes. In addition he is paid a 50€ bonus if the sale is over 500€.

a The total price that one customer pays for pizzas is 499€.
How much commission does Giovanni earn on this sale?

b If Giovanni can persuade this customer to spend another 10€ on pizzas,
How much **more** will Giovanni earn?

c The total price that another customer pays for pizzas is 750€.
How much does Giovanni earn on this sale?

5 Giovanni buys a new van to deliver the pizzas.
The van costs 8400€ plus VAT which is 17.5%.

a Without using a calculator, work out the total cost of his van.

b Giovanni's brother is a car salesman. He offers Giovanni two different deals.

20% off the price of a van, **including** VAT   OR   5% off the price of a van, **excluding** VAT

Which is the best deal for Giovanni?

4a

4b

4a

5b

5.1 Averages

1 Work out the answers to these.

    a $3078 + 1885$ **b** $3078 - 1885$ **c** 3078×5 **d** $1885 \div 5$

2 Maggie asked nine friends how many music CDs they bought last year.
Their answers were: 11   13   11   20   14   8   14   8   11

Work out
a the range of the number of music CDs bought
b the mode of the number of music CDs bought.

(4b)

3 Glen carried out a survey of the amount of money pupils spent on lunch in the school canteen. Here are his results.

Amount spent	£0–£0.49	£0.50–£0.99	£1.00–£1.49	£1.50–£1.99	£2.00–£2.50
Number of pupils	9	28	32	18	13

What is the modal class?

(4a)

4 These are the times, in seconds, taken by ten pupils to run 100 m.
16 , 14 , 18 , 15 , 19 , 18 , 16 , 21 , 15 , 18
Work out

    a the mean time taken   **b** the median time taken.

(5c)

5 A riding stables records the number of riders they have each day.
The costs of the different rides at the stables are £15, £25 and £30.
This table shows the number of riders on each ride on one day.

Cost of ride	Number of riders
£15	5
£25	9
£30	6

Calculate the mean cost per rider.

(5c)

6 Bronwen carried out a survey of the amount of money ten of her friends earned for part-time jobs.
Here are her results.
£9.50, £32.50, £6.50, £20.50, £0, £19, £8, £20.50, £7, £8.50

    a Find the mode, median, mean and range.
    b Which is the best measure of average to use for this data?
       Comment on your choice.

(6c)

7 A company that runs helicopter trips weigh all of their customers.
This table shows the mass of the customers on one day.

What is the modal class?

Mass (m kg)	Number of customers
$30 \leqslant m < 40$	2
$40 \leqslant m < 50$	9
$50 \leqslant m < 60$	7
$60 \leqslant m < 70$	11
$70 \leqslant m < 80$	13
$80 \leqslant m < 90$	12
$90 \leqslant m < 100$	6

(6c)

5.2 Charts 1

1 a Write seventeen thousand eight hundred and seven in figures.

   b Add together 17.6 and 61.7   **c** Subtract 337 from 629

2 This bar chart shows the amount people spend on fresh fruit and vegetables in one week.
What is the modal group?

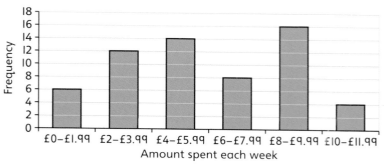

Amount spent each week

4c

3 This bar-line graph shows where people buy their fruit and vegetables each week.

   a How many people buy their fruit and vegetables from a farm shop?

   b How many **more** people buy their fruit and vegetables from a greengrocer than from a market stall?

   c What is the mode?

Type of shop

4b

4 The compound bar chart shows the number of hot drinks sold in 'Carol's cafe'.
It shows the number of teas and coffees sold at lunchtime in one week.

   a On which day were the most drinks sold?

   b On which day were the most teas sold?

   c How many coffees were sold on Saturday?

   d On which two days were the same number of coffees sold?

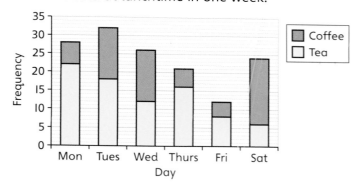

Day

5b

5 'Carol's cafe' sells four types of cake: banana, carrot, chocolate and fruit.
This table gives information on the number of each type sold one weekend.

	Saturday	Sunday
banana	5	8
carrot	7	11
chocolate	8	2
fruit	9	6

   a Draw a compound bar chart to show this information.

   b On which day were the most cakes sold?

   c Which is the most popular type of cake? Explain your answer.

5a

5.3 Charts 2

1 Put the correct sign, > or <, between each pair of numbers.

a 4.42 ☐ 4.24   b 0.056 ☐ 0.05   c 18.6 ☐ 18.66   d 86p ☐ £0.95

2 Here is a line graph showing the maximum monthly temperatures in Cardiff in 2006.

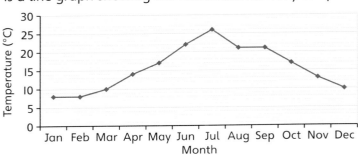

a Which month had the highest maximum temperature?

b Which two months had a maximum temperature of 21°C?

c Find the difference between the maximum temperatures in May and June.

3 This table shows the minimum monthly temperatures in Cardiff in 2006.

Month	Jan	Feb	Mar	Apr	May	Jun	Jul	Aug	Sep	Oct	Nov	Dec
Temperature (°C)	3	2	4	6	9	12	15	13	12	9	4	4

a Draw a line graph of these data.

b Which month had the coldest minimum temperature?

c Use your graph and the graph in Q2 to work out:
  i the difference between the maximum and minimum temperatures in July
  ii which month had the smallest difference between maximum and minimum temperatures.

4 This population pyramid shows the number of men and women in each age group in Great Britain in 2004.

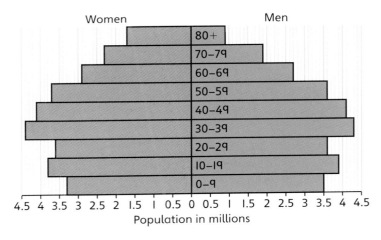

a Which age range has the highest number of
  i women?
  ii men?

b What is the difference between the number of women and men in the age range 70-79?

c Discuss the similarities between the number of women and men in the population of Great Britain in 2004.

5.4 Probability

1 Write these temperatures in order, starting with the coldest.

0°C   −2°C   3°C   −1°C   2°C   −4°C

2 For each outcome, write whether it is impossible, certain, even chance, likely or unlikely.
When you roll an ordinary dice, you will get:

  a a five
  b an odd number
  c a number greater than six
  d a number less than six.
  e a number greater than zero

3 For each outcome, write whether it is impossible, certain, even chance, likely or unlikely.

  a You will get a text message today.
  b You will eat chocolate today.
  c You will win £100 today.
  d You will catch a cold today.
  e You will listen to some music today.

4 Copy this probability scale.

Impossible   Less than even   Even   More than even   Certain

Mark each of these outcomes on the scale by writing the letters **a-e**.
A pupil chosen at random in your class will:

  a be a girl
  b be 18 years old
  c own a mobile phone
  d watch some T.V. today
  e have a younger brother and an older sister.

5 Here is a spinner.
Work out the probability of the spinner landing on:

  a green
  b blue
  c red
  d red or blue
  e orange.

6 Here is the word PROBABILITY.
List all the possible outcomes if a letter is picked at random.

7 Here is a bag of coloured counters.
List all the possible outcomes if one
counter is picked at random.

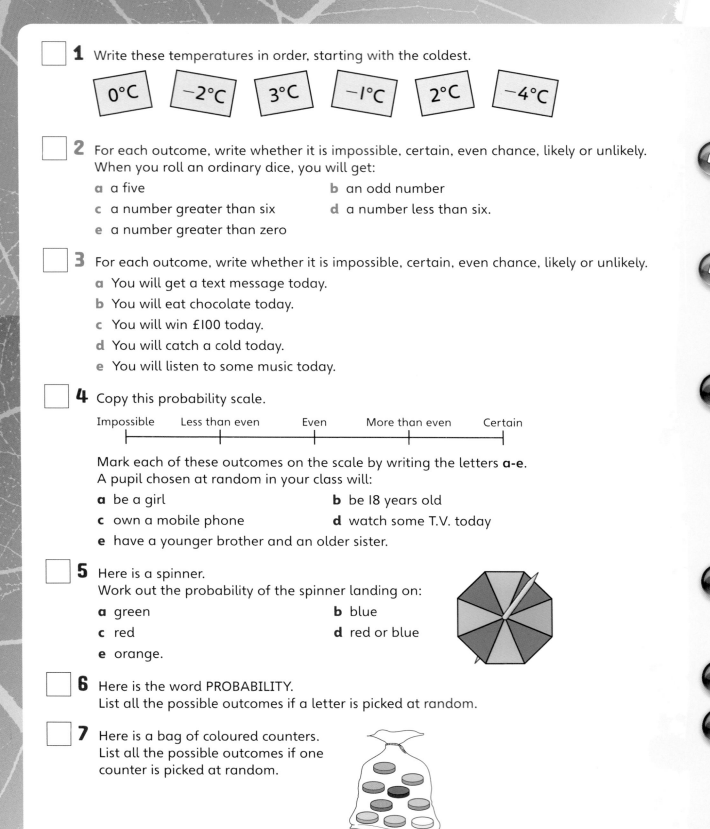

4a

4a

5c

5b

5b

5b

5.5 Experimental probability

1 Which is greater, $\frac{1}{4}$ of £24 or $\frac{1}{7}$ of £35? Show your working.

2 Rhys threw a coin 20 times. He recorded whether the coin landed on heads or tails.
Here are the results of his experiment.

	Heads	Tails
Frequency	12	8

Display this information in a bar chart.

3 Bethan rolled a four-sided dice. She recorded the number on the dice.
Here are the results of her experiment.

Number on dice	1	2	3	4
Frequency	6	8	5	11

a How many times did she roll the dice?

b Display this information on a bar-line graph.

4 Use the data in Q3 to work out these estimated probabilities.
When Bethan rolls the dice she will get:

a a three   **b** a four   **c** an even number   **d** not a 1.

5 Here is a spinner.

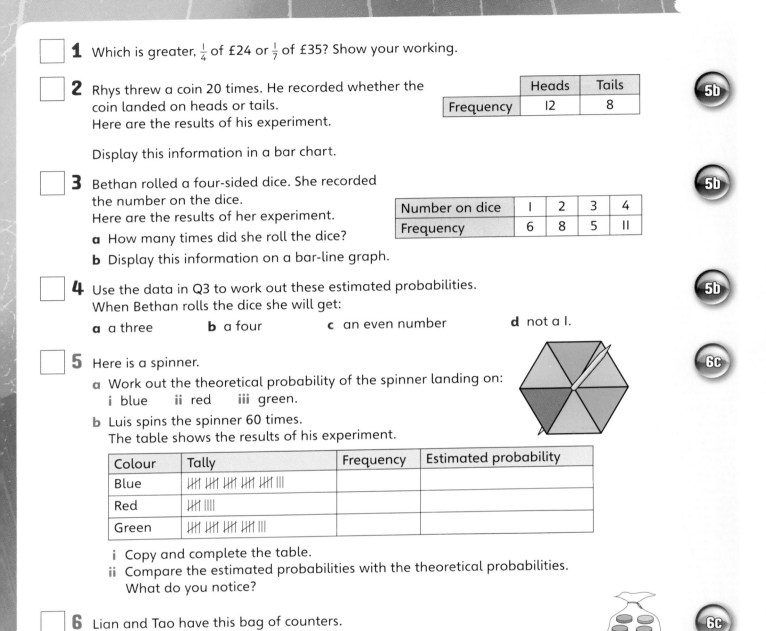

a Work out the theoretical probability of the spinner landing on:
   i blue   **ii** red   **iii** green.

b Luis spins the spinner 60 times.
The table shows the results of his experiment.

Colour	Tally	Frequency	Estimated probability
Blue	IIII IIII IIII IIII IIII III		
Red	IIII IIII		
Green	IIII IIII IIII IIII III		

   i Copy and complete the table.
   ii Compare the estimated probabilities with the theoretical probabilities.
      What do you notice?

6 Lian and Tao have this bag of counters.

a Work out the theoretical probability of choosing at random a counter that is:
   i pink   **ii** orange   **iii** yellow.

b Lian and Tao take a counter at random from the bag, write down the colour, then put the counter back in the bag. They do this 30 times each.

Lian
Colour	Pink	Orange	Yellow
Frequency	17	11	2

Tao
Colour	Pink	Orange	Yellow
Frequency	14	9	7

These tables show the results of their experiment.
   i Compare the results of Lian and Tao. What do you notice?
      Use the words of probability; more likely, less likely, even chance, etc.
   ii Compare the results of Lian and Tao with the theoretical probabilities
      you found in part **a**. What do you notice?

Play any game on the LiveText CD.

5.6 All for charity

1 Which of these shapes has the equivalent of $\frac{3}{4}$ shaded?

a   **b**   **c** 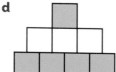 **d**

2 a Make a four-sided spinner by cutting out a
square of paper or card about this size.
Number your spinner as shown.
Put a cocktail stick (or similar)
through the middle.
(Don't use an unused match!)

b Spin your spinner 20 times.
Record your results in a frequency table like this.

Score	Tally	Frequency
1		
2		
3		
4		

c Estimate the probability of your spinner landing on '3'.
Write your answer as a fraction and as a percentage.

d Do you think your spinner is fair? Give a reason for your answer.

3 This fair spinner is spun once.
What is the probability that the spinner will land on

a a six

b a red section

c a green section with an even number

d a red section with not an odd number

e a white section with an even number

f not a green section?

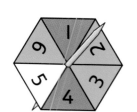

4 Dylan is at the school charity event.
He decides to try the Lucky Dip.
He is told that in the bucket there are 70 small boxes.
One of the small boxes contains a £20 note.
All the other boxes are empty.

a He takes out one box. What is the probability he
will win the £20 note?

b How many boxes would he need to take out in order to give himself a 10% chance of
winning?

6.1 Mappings and expressions

1 The number 48 has 10 factors.
Copy and complete this factor diagram.
Some of the factors have been found for you.
Find as many of the other factors as you can.

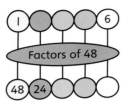

2 Using m as a mystery number, write expressions for:

   a the number multiplied by 6   **b** 4 added to the number

   c the number squared   **d** the number subtracted from 10.

3 Here are some coloured rods. Their lengths are shown as algebraic expressions.

   $2q + 3$ $3q - 1$ $q + 9$

Write expressions for the total length of the rods shown. Simplify your expressions.

  a   **b**

  c   **d**

4 **a** Copy this circle.
Use a compass to draw the circle.
The circle must have a radius of 4.8 cm.
Put a mark every 1 cm around the edge
of the circle and number the marks 1 to 30.

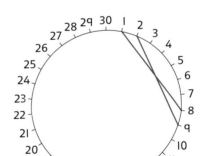

   b On the circle draw mapping diagrams for
these functions.

     i $x \longrightarrow x + 7$ **ii** $x \longrightarrow 2x$

   Use a different colour for each function.
The first one has been started for you.

5 Use these mappings to fill in the missing outputs.

   a $x \longrightarrow 3x + 1$ **b** $x \longrightarrow \dfrac{x + 5}{2}$ **c** $x \longrightarrow 2 - x$

     $1 \longrightarrow \ldots$ $1 \longrightarrow \ldots$ $0 \longrightarrow \ldots$

     $2 \longrightarrow \ldots$ $3 \longrightarrow \ldots$ $-5 \longrightarrow \ldots$

6 Use these mappings to fill in the missing inputs.

   a $x \longrightarrow 2x + 10$ **b** $x \longrightarrow \dfrac{x}{2} - 2$ **c** $x \longrightarrow 2 - x$

     $\ldots \longrightarrow 12$ $\ldots \longrightarrow 3$ $\ldots \longrightarrow 0$

     $\ldots \longrightarrow 20$ $\ldots \longrightarrow 0$ $\ldots \longrightarrow -5$

7 In a furniture shop, four members of staff were
asked to work over the Christmas holiday.
The table shows the extra pay they received.

Hours worked (h)	Extra pay
12	£144
31	£372
6.5	£78
12.5	£150

   a What is the mapping that connects the number of
hours worked (h) and the extra pay?

   b If another member of staff worked 15 hours in the
Christmas holiday, how much extra pay would they receive?

6.2 Powers

1 Lien buys 3 identical packets of sweets for £2.46

   a How much does each packet cost?

   b Jin buys 4 packets of the same sweets. How much do his sweets cost?

   c Jin pays with a £5 note. How much change does he get?

2 a Copy this secret code box.

$$\overline{125} \quad \overline{27} \; \overline{36} \; \overset{V}{\overline{25}} \; \overline{9} \quad \overline{64} \; \overline{27} \; \overline{9} \quad \overline{4} \; \overline{8} \; \overline{49} \; \overline{9} \; \overline{81} \quad !$$

   b Work out the answers to these questions.
Put the letter by each question on the line
above the answer in the secret code box.
The first one is done for you.
What is the secret message?

$5^2 = V$	$4^3 = T$	$5^3 = I$
$2^2 = P$	$7^2 = W$	$3^2 = E$
$3^3 = H$	$6^2 = A$	$2^3 = O$
$9^2 = R$		

3 Work out the value of:

   a $\sqrt{36}$ **b** $\sqrt{121}$ **c** $\sqrt[3]{27}$ **d** $\sqrt[3]{216}$

   e $\sqrt{0.04}$ **f** $\sqrt{1.44}$ **g** $\sqrt[3]{64\,000}$ **h** $\sqrt[3]{0.125}$

4 a Copy this table.

Question	Working	Answer
i $4^2 \div 8$	4×125	16
ii $2^3 \times 9$	$64 \div 4$	2
iii 4×5^3	$16 \div 8$	500
iv $8^2 \div 4$	$100 \div 5$	72
v $10^2 \div 5$	8×9	20

   b Draw a line linking the question on the left, to the working in the middle,
to the answer on the right.
The first one has been done for you.

5 Write the following using index notation.

   a $a \times a \times a \times b \times b$ **b** $f \times f \times f \times f \times f \times g \times g \times g$

   c $3 \times v \times v \times 2 \times w \times w$ **d** $4 \times p \times p \times p \times 5 \times q$

6 Work out the value of $x^2 - 2x$ when:

   a $x = 4$ **b** $x = 5$ **c** $x = 6$

7 These cards show algebraic expressions.
The pink cards are unsimplified and the yellow cards are simplified.
Match each pink card to the correct yellow card.

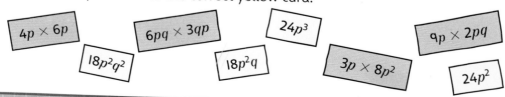

6.3 Using brackets

1 Copy this number grid.
Work your way cross the grid by shading
one square at a time.
You can only go up or down or to the right.
You can only shade prime numbers.
You must start on square S, and finish on square F.
The first two moves have been shaded for you.

S	2	39	25	55	14	37
4	5	42	29	2	31	45
8	11	23	17	63	19	12
32	51	18	22	34	3	48
49	60	51	1	8	7	31
61	35	30	42	10	36	F

2 Copy and complete these multiplications.

　a $2 \times (20 + 4) = 2 \times 20 + 2 \times \ldots = 40 + \ldots = \ldots$

　b $3 \times (30 + 2) = \ldots \times 30 + \ldots \times 2 = \ldots + 6 = \ldots$

　c $5 \times (40 - 7) = 5 \times \ldots - \ldots \times \ldots = \ldots - \ldots = \ldots$

3 a Copy this table.

	Question	Working	Working	Answer
i	8×32	$6 \times (50 + 4)$	$280 - 8$	324
ii	3×49	$4 \times (70 - 2)$	$300 + 24$	272
iii	6×54	$8 \times (30 + 2)$	$150 - 3$	256
iv	4×68	$3 \times (50 - 1)$	$240 + 16$	147

　b Draw a line linking the question on the left, to the steps of working in the
middle, to the answer on the right.
The first one has been done for you.

4 Simplify these expressions by multiplying out the brackets.

　a $3(x + 8)$　　　b $6(b - 9)$　　　c $4(7 + 3h)$　　　d $5(2i + 3k)$

5 These cards show algebraic expressions.
Match each blue card to the correct yellow card.

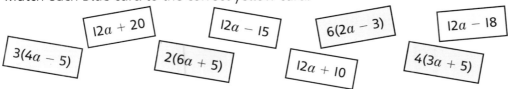

$12a + 20$　　$12a - 15$　　$6(2a - 3)$　　$12a - 18$

$3(4a - 5)$　　$2(6a + 5)$　　$12a + 10$　　$4(3a + 5)$

6 Simplify these expressions by multiplying out the brackets.

　a $x(x + 2)$　　　b $b(b - 7)$　　　c $4h(2 + 6h)$　　　d $6i(3i - 9)$

7 Here are two rods.

　$\leftarrow x + 5 \rightarrow$　　　$\leftarrow 2y - 4 \rightarrow$

　a Use brackets to write expressions for the total length of:
　　i 3 red rods　　ii 4 blue rods

　b Simplify your expressions in part a by multiplying out the brackets.

6.4 Substituting into formulae

1 The number 80 has 10 factors.
Copy and complete this factor diagram.
Some of the factors have been found for you.

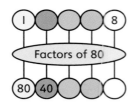

2 The formula to work out the total number of horseshoes needed at a riding stable is:

> number of horseshoes = 4 × number of horses

Use this formula to work out the number of horseshoes needed if there are:
a 10 horses **b** 20 horses **c** 50 horses.

3 The formula to work out the total number of nails needed for the horseshoes is:

> number of nails = 7 × number of horseshoes

Use this formula to work out the number of nails needed if there are:
a 4 shoes **b** 10 shoes **c** 20 shoes.

4 Find the value of these expressions when $p = 3$ and $q = 6$.
a $p + q$ **b** $q \div p$ **c** $4q$ **d** $20 - q - 2p$

5 The area of a triangle is worked out using the formula:

$$\text{Area} = \frac{b \times h}{2}$$
where: b is the base of the triangle
h is the height of the triangle

Work out the area of a triangle with:
a a base of 8 cm and a height of 6 cm **b** a base of 9 cm and a height of 4 cm

6 Find the value of these expressions when $r = -2$ and $t = 5$.
a $3r + t$ **b** $4t \div r$ **c** $5r + 10$ **d** $30 + 7r - 5t$

7 The pink cards are question cards and the yellow cards are answer cards.
Using $e = 3$ and $f = 4$, work out the values of the expressions on the question cards.
Match each pink card to the correct yellow card.

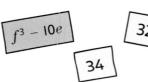

$2f^2$ 35 $e^3 + 2f$ 36 $4e^2$ $f^3 - 10e$ 34 32

6.5 Deriving formulae

1 Put the correct sign, > or <, between each pair of numbers.

    a $-4 \boxed{} 5$ **b** $6 \boxed{} -9$ **c** $-13 \boxed{} -8$ **d** $0 \boxed{} -3$

2 Sally buys two more bread rolls than the number of people she invites to dinner.

    a Work out the number of bread rolls Sally buys if she invites
        i 4 people to dinner   **ii** 8 people to dinner

    b Write down a formula that connects the number of bread rolls, **R**, to the number of people she invites to dinner, **P**.

(5c)

3 Greg feeds his dogs two tins of dog food each day.

    a Work out the number of tins of dog food Greg needs to buy to feed his dogs for:
        i 7 days   **ii** 10 days

    b Write down a formula that connects the number of tins of dog food, T, that Greg needs to buy to feed his dogs for D days.

(5c)

4 Carlos buys milk from a supermarket.
Find the total cost of the milk he buys when:

    a he buys 2 litres costing 45 pence per litre.

    b he buys 3 litres costing 48 pence per litre.

    c he buys x litres costing y pence per litre.

    d Write a formula to work out the total cost, C, of buying x litres of milk costing y pence per litre.

(5b)

5 Fola buys a CD and a DVD each month.
Find the total cost each month when Fola buys:

    a a CD costing £12 and a DVD costing £15   **b** a CD costing £13 and a DVD costing £16

    c a CD costing £**c** and a DVD costing £**d**

    d Write a formula to work out the total cost, **T**, of buying a CD costing £**c** and a DVD costing £**d**.

(5b)

6 Kesia works out the mean age of two members of her family.
Find the mean age of the two members of her family when they are:

    a 6 years old and 14 years old.

    b 50 years old and 84 years old.

    c h years old and k years old.

    d Write a formula to work out the mean age, A, of two people who are h years old and k years old.

(5a)

7 Brendan joins a bowls club.
He pays a membership fee, and then £3 for each game he plays.
Work out the total cost for Brendan when:

    a the membership fee is £15 and he plays 8 games.

    b the membership fee is £18 and he plays 12 games.

    c the membership fee is £**m** and he plays **b** games.

    d Write a formula connecting the total cost, **C**, to the membership fee, **m**, and the number of games played, **b**.

(5a)

7.1 Lines and angles

1 Work out the answers to these, without using a calculator.

a £26.25 + £92.80   **b** £47.59 − £39.64   **c** 345.95 + 7.5

d 5.25 − 1.4   **e** 64.2 + 8.97   **f** 3.8 − 1.25

2 Use the words and numbers in the cloud to complete these sentences.

> 90°   straight   0°   reflex
> 90°   right   180°

a An angle which is exactly 90° is a _____ angle.

b An angle which is more than _____ but less than _____ is an obtuse angle.

c An angle which is exactly 180° is a _____ line.

d An angle which is more than _____ but less than _____ is an acute angle.

e Which word from the cloud haven't you used?
Write a sentence that describes this word.

3 Look at this diagram and answer the following questions.
Do not use a protractor.

a What type of angles are ∠ABC and ∠BCD.

b Which angle looks less than 45°?

c Which angle looks like a right angle?

d Which two angles look the same size?

4 In this diagram ∠XYZ, ∠WYZ and ∠WYX join together at a point.

a From the list below, choose three angles which could be the angles shown in the diagram:
56°, 65°, 138°, 142°, 153°, 247°

b Explain why you chose these three angles.

5 Work out the value of angles m and n in these triangles.

a   42° $m°$

b   105°   45° $n°$

6 In △PQR, PR and PQ are 5 cm, and RQ is 5.6 cm. ∠PRQ and ∠PQR are 56°.
Sketch △PQR and calculate ∠RPQ.

7 Work out the value of angles x, y, p, q, and r in these diagrams.
Show your calculations and explain how you found each answer.

a $y°$ 32° $x°$

b   95°   146° $p°$ $r°$ $q°$

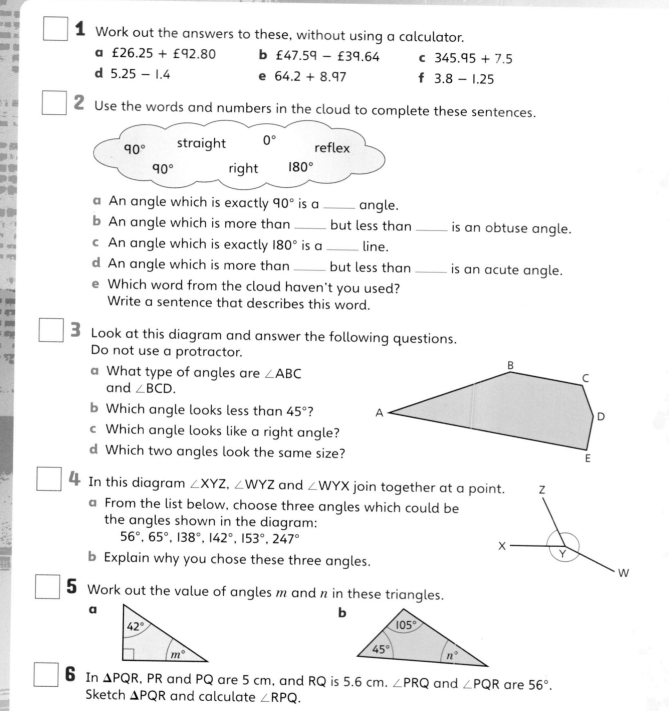

7.2 Angle rules

1 At midnight the temperature in Birmingham was −4°C.
By midday the next day the temperature had risen to 5°C.
By how many degrees did the temperature rise?

2 Work out the value of angles x, y, and z in these diagrams.
Show your calculations.

a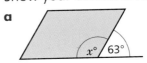

b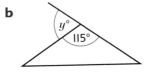

c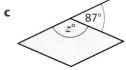

5c

3 a Complementary angles add up to 90°, so 30° is the complement of 60°.
Find the complement of:
   i 70°   **ii** 42°   **iii** 4°   **iv** 78°

b Supplementary angles add up to 180°, so 30° is the supplement of 150°.
Find the supplement of:
   i 50°   **ii** 168°   **iii** 5°   **iv** 97°

5b

4 Work out the value of angles p, q, and r in these diagrams.
Show your calculations.

a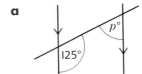

b

c

5b

5 Work out the value of angles a, b, c, d, e and f in this diagram.

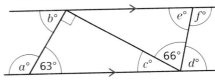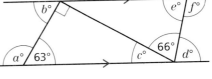

6c

6 Use this diagram to show that the
angles in a quadrilateral sum to 360°.
Remember to use the fact that the
angles in a triangle sum to 180°.

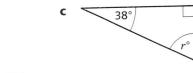

6b

7 Look at this diagram.
Copy and complete these sentences to show that
the exterior angle of a triangle is equal to the sum
of the two interior opposite angles.
Angles a, b and c lie within a _____ so add up to _____.
Angles c and d lie on a _____ _____ so add up to _____.
So $a + b + c = $ _____ + _____
Subtract c from both sides to give _____ + _____ = _____.

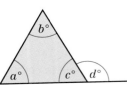

6a

7.3 Coordinates

1 Work out these multiplications.
Use the grid method in parts **a** and **b**, and the standard method in parts **c** and **d**.

a 376 × 3   b 782 × 6   c 329 × 4   d 521 × 5

2 Write down the letter that is next to each of the following points.

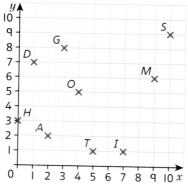

(7, 1)   (2, 2) (9, 6)   (3, 8) (4, 5) (4, 5) (1, 7)

(2, 2) (5, 1)   (5, 1) (0, 3) (7, 1) (10, 9)

What have you written?

3 Copy the axes in Q2.
Plot these points on the grid and join each in turn with a straight line.

(1, 3) (1, 7) (5, 7) (5, 9) (9, 5) (5, 1) (5, 3) (1, 3)

What have you drawn?

4 Write down the number or symbol that is next to each of the following points.

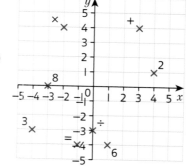

(−4, −3) (−2, 4) (1, −4) (3, 4) (−3, 0) (0, −3) (4, 1) (−1, −4)

Work out the answer to the calculation you have written.

5 Copy the axes in Q4.
Plot these points on the grid and join each in turn with a straight line.

(0, 4) (4, 1) (2, −3) (−2, −3) (−4, 1) (0, 4)

What shape have you drawn?

6 Look at this diagram.

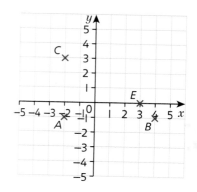

  a Find the midpoint for each of these lines and write down its coordinates:
    i AB   **ii** AC
  b E is the midpoint of CD.
    What are the coordinates of the point D?

7 **a** Copy the axes in Q4.
    Plot these points on the grid: A(−4, 0) B(−3, 2) C(1, 1)
  b You can make a quadrilateral by adding an extra point D.
    What are the coordinates of point D if the quadrilateral formed is:
    i a rectangle?   **ii** a parallelogram?

4a

4a

5c

5b

6c

6c

8.1 Planning data collection

1 Will's age can be divided by five, but not by ten.
Will is three years older than Tim. The sum of their ages is divisible by 3. Both of them are younger than 30.
How old are Will and Tim?

2 Abu wants to find out the favourite pet of the other pupils in his class.

   a What questions should Abu ask, and who should he ask?

   b What answer options should Abu provide?

   c Design a suitable data collection sheet.
Include columns to record the tally and frequency.

4a

3 Nia wants to investigate the number of pets that pupils in her year group own.
There are 170 pupils in Nia's year group.

   a Design a suitable data collection sheet that she could use.

   b Describe how she could carry out her investigation.

4a

4 Kim wants to find out how many pupils in her school say that P.E. is their favourite subject.
There are 800 pupils in her school.
How many pupils should Kim ask? Explain your answer.

5a

5 Tanisha wants to draw a graph to show the heights of her 20 sunflower plants.
The shortest plant is 1.13 m and the tallest plant is 2.06 m.
Design a data collection sheet for this continuous data.
Start with a height interval of $1.10 \leqslant h < 1.20$.

5a

6 Cathy is training to become a veterinary nurse.
She has to carry out a health-check on puppies when they are six weeks old.
As part of the health check she has to weigh the puppies.

   a What units should she use?

   b What type of data is Cathy collecting?

   c Design a suitable grouped data collection sheet that she could use.

6c

7 Design a data collection sheet to record the number of pairs of shoes that pupils in your class own.

6c

8.2 Questionnaires

1 Copy and complete this multiplication grid.

×	4		6	
5	40			
	16			
7			21	
9				

2 Jorgen wants to find out what his friends' favourite hobbies are.
He writes a questionnaire and splits it into different sections for different hobbies.

    a List some of the hobbies that Jorgen should put in his section for

        i sports   **ii** clubs   **iii** music

        iv computer games   **v** reading

    b Add more options to this section of Jorgen's questionnaire.

> What type of music do you like to listen to best?
>
> Rock 'n' roll   ☐
>
> Club   ☐
>
> Classical   ☐
>
> .....

3 Kajsa wants to find out what type of books her friends like to read.

    a List some types of books Kajsa could put into her question.

    b Make up a question, with response boxes, that Kajsa could use.

4 Katarina wants to find out what her friends' favourite birthday presents were.

    a List some of the presents Katarina could put into her question.

    b Make up a question, with response boxes, that Katarina could use.

5 Greta wants to find out how much fruit people eat.

    a What time scale should Greta use?

    b What ranges should Greta use to collect her grouped data?

    c Write a question that Greta could use.

    d Who should she ask?

6 Greger wants to find out about young peoples' favourite sport.

    a Explain why it would not be a good idea to stand outside the local swimming pool to ask this question.

    b Where would be a better place to carry out his survey?

    c List some sports that Greger could use in his question.

    d Make up a question, with response boxes, that Greger could use.

5c

5c

5c

6c

6c

8.3 Collecting data

1 a Write down the numbers from the cloud that are square numbers.

  b i Write down the numbers from the cloud that aren't square numbers.

   ii Add these numbers together.

   iii Is this total a square number?

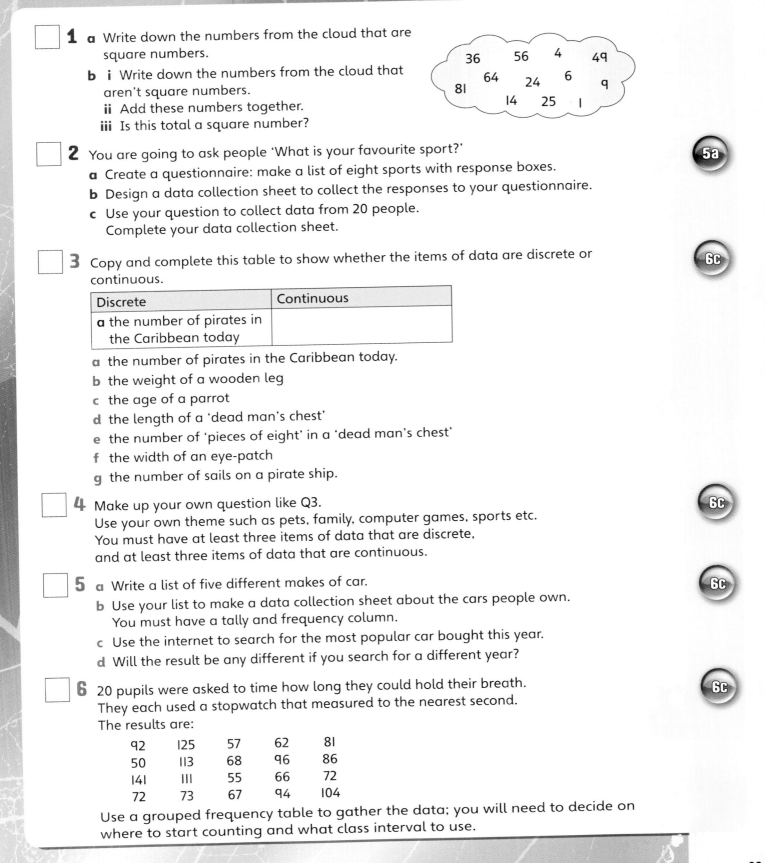

36   56   4   49
64   24   6
81   9
14   25   1

2 You are going to ask people 'What is your favourite sport?'

  a Create a questionnaire: make a list of eight sports with response boxes.

  b Design a data collection sheet to collect the responses to your questionnaire.

  c Use your question to collect data from 20 people. Complete your data collection sheet.

3 Copy and complete this table to show whether the items of data are discrete or continuous.

Discrete	Continuous
a the number of pirates in the Caribbean today	

  a the number of pirates in the Caribbean today.

  b the weight of a wooden leg

  c the age of a parrot

  d the length of a 'dead man's chest'

  e the number of 'pieces of eight' in a 'dead man's chest'

  f the width of an eye-patch

  g the number of sails on a pirate ship.

4 Make up your own question like Q3.
Use your own theme such as pets, family, computer games, sports etc.
You must have at least three items of data that are discrete,
and at least three items of data that are continuous.

5 a Write a list of five different makes of car.

  b Use your list to make a data collection sheet about the cars people own. You must have a tally and frequency column.

  c Use the internet to search for the most popular car bought this year.

  d Will the result be any different if you search for a different year?

6 20 pupils were asked to time how long they could hold their breath.
They each used a stopwatch that measured to the nearest second.
The results are:

92	125	57	62	81
50	113	68	96	86
141	111	55	66	72
72	73	67	94	104

Use a grouped frequency table to gather the data; you will need to decide on where to start counting and what class interval to use.

8.4 Interpreting charts

1 Work out the answers to these.

   a 0.2 × 3   **b** 7 × 0.4   **c** 8 × 0.01   **d** 0.06 × 4

2 Here is a pictogram.
It shows the number of people that went to the 'early morning swim' at a swimming pool one week.

  a Write down the number of people who went to the 'early morning swim' on

Monday	⦿ ⦿ ⦿ ⦿ ⦿
Tuesday	⦿ ⦿ ⦿ ⦿ ☾
Wednesday	⦿ ⦿ ⦿ ◞
Thursday	⦿ ⦿ ◖
Friday	

⦿ represents 4 people

    i Monday   **ii** Tuesday
    iii Wednesday   **iv** Thursday.

  b 15 people went to the 'early morning swim' on Friday. Draw a diagram to show this.

3 Sheena and Siobhan join a slimming club.
This bar chart shows the number of calories they consumed in one week.

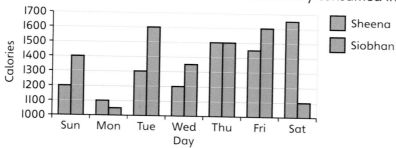

  a How many calories did Sheena consume on Wednesday?

  b On which day did Sheena and Siobhan consume the same number of calories?

  c On which day was there the biggest difference between the number of calories that Sheena and Siobhan consumed?

  d Who consumed the most calories during the week? Explain your answer.

4 Alex asked his friends who their favourite James Bond actor was.
This pie chart shows his results.

  a Which actor did Alex's friends like best?

  b Which actor did one quarter of Alex's friends like?

  c Which actors did Alex's friends like equally?

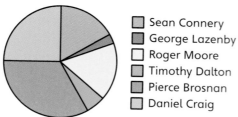

- Sean Connery
- George Lazenby
- Roger Moore
- Timothy Dalton
- Pierce Brosnan
- Daniel Craig

8.5 Pie charts and line graphs

1 A return flight to Colorado in America costs £558 per person.
How much does it cost a group of six people to fly to Colorado?

2 A women's clothes shop sells the
following number of dresses in one day.

   a Copy and complete the table.

   b Draw a pie chart for this information.

Dress size	Frequency	Number of degrees
10	3	
12	10	
14	8	
16	15	
Totals	36	360°

3 A men's clothes shop sells the following
number of T-shirts in one day.

   a Copy and complete the table.

   b Draw a pie chart for this information.

T-shirt size	Frequency	Number of degrees
XS	8	
S	12	
M	60	
L	35	
XL	5	
Totals	120	360°

4 Caroline uses this graph to convert between British pounds (£) and US dollars ($).

   a How many dollars can she
buy with £10?

   b How many pounds does a
$32 T-shirt cost?

   c Work out how many dollars
Caroline can get for £120.

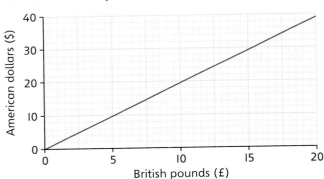

5 A farmer compares these line graphs.
Comment on the relationship between milk production and hours of sunshine in 2007.

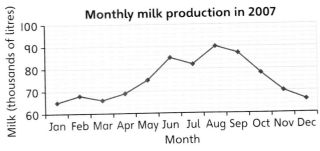

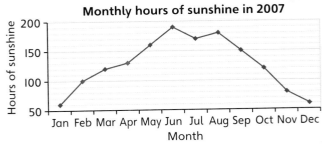

Play any game on the LiveText CD.

9.1 Place value and rounding whole numbers

1 Look at the table below,
The column on the left has numbers written in words.
The column on the right has numbers written in figures.
Match each number on the left with the correct number on the right.
The first one has been done for you.

	Number in words
A	zero point four two
B	zero point two four two
C	zero point four two two
D	zero point zero four two
E	zero point two four
F	zero point zero two two four

	Number in figures
G	0.24
H	0.422
I	0.42
J	0.0224
K	0.242
L	0.042

A matches I

2 Round these numbers to the nearest 10.

   a 47　　　　　**b** 85　　　　　**c** 172　　　　　**d** 4069

3 Round these numbers to the nearest 100.

   a 734　　　　**b** 890　　　　**c** 1450　　　　**d** 12 609

4 The numbers on the yellow cards have been rounded to the nearest 1 000 to give the numbers on the pink cards.

2450　　5000　　1398　　3000　　6000　　3940　　2565　　1000　　4000　　4500　　2000

   a Match each yellow card with the correct pink card.

   b Which pink card is left over?

   c Write down a number that you can round to the nearest 1000 to give the number on this pink card.

5 The table shows the total length of the railways in three countries.

Write these lengths to the nearest 10 000.

Country	Total length of railways (km)
USA	226 612
Russia	87 157
China	75 438

6 In 2007, the population of Iceland was estimated to be 301 931, Norway was 4 627 926 and Denmark was 5 468 120. Write these population figures to the nearest 100 000.

7 The total length of the roads in the whole world is estimated to be 32 million km to the nearest million. To the nearest kilometre, what is **a** the **longest** possible total length **b** the **shortest** possible total length of the roads?

8 Write the following as powers of 10:   **a** 1 000　　**b** 10 000 000　　**c** 10

9.2 Rounding and ordering decimals

1 This is a MCC (Mental Challenge Curve). Copy the curve.
Start at the first calculation, then in your head work out the missing values.

2 Round these numbers to the nearest whole number.

   a 2.2   **b** 12.9   **c** 3.75   **d** 14.21

3 The numbers on the green cards have been rounded to one decimal place to give the numbers on the blue cards.

| 4.78 | 5.25 | 4.7 | 5.95 | 5.22 | 5.3 |

| 5.2 | 6.0 | 4.71 | 4.8 | 5.9 |

   a Match each green card with the correct blue card.

   b Which blue card is left over?

   c Write down a number that you can round to one decimal place to give the number on this blue card.

4 Use a calculator to do these. Give your answer to two decimal places.

   a $14 \div 9$ **b** $3 \div 17$ **c** 5.23^2 **d** $\sqrt{18}$

5 The following are answers to calculations. Write the answers to the nearest penny.

   a £35.254   **b** £21.679   **c** £30.799   **d** £85.9939

6 Put these decimal number cards in **descending** order.

| 32.603 | 36.223 | 36.02 | 36.3 | 32.566 | 32.63 |

7 Choose the correct answer **or** answers for each of these.
The first one is done for you.

   a Given that $12.56 \leqslant m \leqslant 12.61$, m could be:

     A 12.63 ✗   B 12.59 ✓   C 12.56 ✓

   b Given that $83.22 \leqslant n \leqslant 83.55$, n could be:

     A 83.21   B 83.61   C 83.38

   c Given that $9.79 \leqslant p \leqslant 9.93$, p could be:

     A 9.93   B 9.88   C 9.9

   d Given that $28.26 \leqslant q \leqslant 28.8$, q could be:

     A 28.85   B 28.19   C 28.59

4b

4a

5a

5a

6c

6a

9.3 Measures

1 Write the value in words of the four in each of these numbers.

    a 24.56   **b** 13.94   **c** 125.481   **d** 0.074

2 Write down the number the arrow is pointing to.

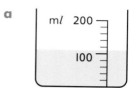 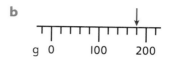

    a   **b**   **c**

    cm 59   60   mm 40   50   60   m   2   2.5

3 Write down the value shown on each of these scales.

    a   **b**   **c**

    ml 200   40

    100   g 0   100   200   30   kg   50

4 The diagram shows a tyre pressure gauge.
Tyre pressures can be measured
in psi (pounds per square inch).

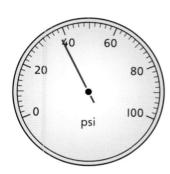

    a Write down the value shown on this gauge.

    b Copy the tyre pressure gauge and draw arrows
        on it to show the following pressures.

        i 52 psi   **ii** 76 psi   **iii** 95 psi

5 Convert these amounts into the units shown.

    a 4.6 m = _____ cm   **b** 25 mm = _____ cm   **c** 8.5 km = _____ m

    d 6500 ml = _____ l   **e** 0.6 kg = _____ g   **f** 45 cl = _____ ml

    g 652 cm = _____ m   **h** 12.6 l = _____ cl   **i** 12 600 m = _____ km

6   5 miles ≈ 8 km

    Caitlin drives 25 miles from her home to work.

    a How many kilometres is this?

    b She drives to work and back five days a week.
        How many kilometres does she drive to work and back in one week?

7   I ounce ≈ 30 g   I pint ≈ 500 ml

    a A recipe uses 4 ounces of sugar. How many grams is this?

    b The same recipe uses half a pint of milk. How many ml is this?

9.4 Mental methods

1 Put these lengths in order of size, starting with the shortest.

 3000 mm   2.65 m   0.025 km   245 cm   2.7 m   292 cm

2 Use this fact $356 × 0.2 = 71.2$ to answer these:
   a $35.6 × 0.2$ **b** $0.356 × 2$ **c** $3.56 × 20$ **d** $3560 × 0.02$

3 Use partitioning to multiply these:
   a $82 × 7$ **b** $95 × 0.4$ **c** $23 × 1.6$ **d** $65 × 2.2$

4 a Copy this table.

	Question	Working	Answer
i	$16 × 6$	$0.6 × 7$	13.2
ii	$2.5 × 12$	$9 × 9$	96
iii	$4.5 × 18$	$8 × 12$	30
iv	$1.2 × 3.5$	$11 × 1.2$	4.2
v	$5.5 × 2.4$	$5 × 6$	81

   b Draw a line linking the question on the left, to the working in the middle, to the answer on the right. Use doubling and halving. The first one has been done for you.

5 Write **true** or **false** for each of these:
   a $50^2 = 250$ **b** $0.4^2 = 0.16$ **c** $600^2 = 360\,000$
   d $0.01^2 = 0.001$ **e** $1.1^2 = 1.21$ **f** $0.7^2 = 4.9$

6 Use the numbers in the cloud to complete these multiplications.
   You can use each number in the cloud once only.
   a $62 × 0.1 = \boxed{}$ **b** $6.2 × 0.1 = \boxed{}$
   c $6.2 × 0.01 = \boxed{}$ **d** $6200 × 0.1 = \boxed{}$
   e $0.62 × 0.01 = \boxed{}$ **f** $6200 × 0.01 = \boxed{}$

   0.0062   62   620   6.2   0.62   0.062

7 Arrange these cards into three groups of equivalent expressions.

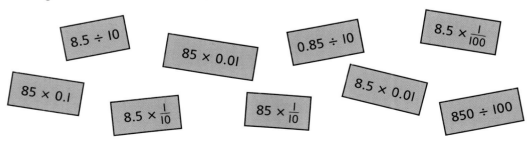

$8.5 ÷ 10$ $85 × 0.01$ $0.85 ÷ 10$ $8.5 × \frac{1}{100}$ $85 × 0.1$ $8.5 × \frac{1}{10}$ $85 × \frac{1}{10}$ $8.5 × 0.01$ $850 ÷ 100$

9.5 Written multiplication

1 Copy and complete this table.
The first one is done for you.

	Old temperature	Change in temperature	New temperature
a	2°C	4°C colder	−2°C
b	−3°C	3°C warmer	
c	−4°C	2°C colder	
d	5°C	7°C colder	
e	−7°C	9°C warmer	

2 a Estimate the answers to these questions.
   i 542 × 78   **ii** 631 × 29

  b Copy the grids and use them to work out the answers to the questions.
    i 542 × 78   **ii** 631 × 29

×	500	40	2
70			
8			

×	600	30	1
20			
9			

3 Use any written method to do these multiplications.

  a   4 3 2
     ×   6 5
    ─────

  b   2 8 1
     ×   5 8
    ─────

4 Use the grid method or the standard method to work out the answers to these.

  a 4.2 × 6   **b** 8.9 × 7   **c** 5.16 × 9   **d** 34.42 × 8

5 Work out whether **A**, **B** or **C** is the correct answer to each of these.

  a 0.2 × 0.3 =   **A** 0.6   **B** 0.006   **C** 0.06
  b 0.5 × 0.9 =   **A** 0.45   **B** 0.045   **C** 4.5
  c 0.4 × 0.04 =   **A** 0.16   **B** 0.016   **C** 0.0016
  d 0.08 × 0.07 =   **A** 0.0056   **B** 0.56   **C** 0.056

6 Use the grid method or the standard method to work out the answers to these.

  a 4.2 × 3.6   **b** 8.19 × 0.5   **c** 0.16 × 0.92   **d** 3.42 × 0.28

7 Rosa has spilt coffee on her shopping bill.

> 2 kg broccoli @ £1.78 per kg = £
> 1.5 kg leeks @ £2.28 per kg = £
> 0.65 kg onions @ £0.82 per kg = £
>
>   total cost = £

Use a written method to work out the four missing values.

9.6 Written division

1 In this diagram, opposite numbers add to 100.
Copy and complete the diagram.
The first one has been done for you.

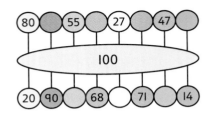

2 Work out these divisions.
Some of them have remainders.

   a 374 ÷ 11   **b** 705 ÷ 15   **c** 830 ÷ 23   **d** 816 ÷ 31

3 Lynn buys pet insurance for her dogs.
She pays £192 for 12 months.
How much does she pay each month?

4 Work out these divisions.

   a 164.2 ÷ 2   **b** 249.6 ÷ 4   **c** 647.5 ÷ 5   **d** 196.8 ÷ 6

5 Pepe has spilt tea on his shopping bill.

> 12 cans of dog food @   per can = £5.04
> 15 cans of cat food @   per can = £4.95
> 14 packs of cat treats @   per pack = £6.72
>   total cost = £16.71

Use a written method to work out the cost per item.

6 Copy this table.

	Question	Equivalent calculation	Answer
i	36.2 ÷ 0.2	6150 ÷ 5	181
ii	24.4 ÷ 0.4	575 ÷ 25	156
iii	61.5 ÷ 0.05	362 ÷ 2	1230
iv	57.5 ÷ 2.5	1872 ÷ 12	61
v	18.72 ÷ 0.12	244 ÷ 4	23

Draw a line linking the question on the left, to the equivalent calculation
in the middle, to the answer on the right.
Use a written method to work the answers out.
The first one has been done for you.

7 Use any written method to work these out.

   a 7.62 ÷ 0.3   **b** 5.16 ÷ 0.4   **c** 52.8 ÷ 1.5   **d** 10.58 ÷ 2.3

9.7 Estimating and order of operations

1 Copy and complete these.

a
```
  4 5 3 2
+ 3 7 6 5
─────────
```

b
```
  2 6 4 9 2
+ 3 5 2 3 8
───────────
```

c
```
  7 5 3 7
- 4 2 6 5
─────────
```

d
```
  6 5 3 9 2
- 2 5 7 4 8
───────────
```

2 Work these out without using a calculator.

a $18 + 2 \times 5$ b $40 - 20 \div 5$ c $12 \div 3 + 12$ d $6 \times 5 - 4 \times 3$

3 Find the value of these.

a $3 \times (4 + 5)$ b $(13 - 9) \times 7$ c $24 \div (11 - 3)$ d $(12 - 7) \times (3 + 4)$

4 Some of these calculations are wrong.

$276 + 463 = 729$	$3772 \div 46 = 81$	$64 \times 29 = 1856$

$9623 \times 9 = 86607$ $8276 - 938 = 7338$

Use inverse operations to find which calculations are wrong.

5 Identify two different approximate calculations for:

a 529×38 b $886 \div 19$ c $974 - 58$ d $51.9 + 124.6$

6 Estimate answers to these. Use a calculator to work out the exact answer.

a $12.2 \times (6.3 + 8.69)$ b $(727 - 472.9) \div 2.1$

c $275.6 + 9.12 \times 27.5$ d $(8.07 + 57) \times (71.6 - 39.4)$

7 a Copy this secret code box.

$$\underline{}\ \underline{}\ \underline{}\ \underset{200}{}\ \underset{15}{}\ \underset{45}{}\ \underset{600}{N}\quad \underset{900}{}\ \underset{80}{}\ \underset{1000}{}\ \underset{200}{}\ \underset{6}{}\ \underset{45}{}\ \underset{1000}{}\ \underset{900}{}\ !$$

```
___ ___ ___  N   ___ ___ ____ ___ __ ___ ____ ___   !
200  15  45 600   900  80 1000 200  6  45 1000 900
```

b Estimate the answers to these questions. Put the letter by each question on the line above the answer in the secret code box. For example, the first estimate is:

$7 \times 80 + 40 = 560 + 40 = 600$,

so N goes above 600 in the table. What is the secret code?

$7 \times 82 + 42$	$= N$
$(103 - 38) \div 4$	$= C$
$67 \times 81 - 61 \times 92$	$= I$
$62 \div (52 - 38)$	$= M$
$211 + 21 \times 39$	$= T$
$(2.16 + 3.07) \times 8.67$	$= A$
$90.14 - 48.36 \div 5.106$	$= S$
$4.86 \times 19.72 + 791.6$	$= E$

Play any game on the LiveText CD.

9.8 Using a calculator

1 Rearrange these decimals in order of size, starting with the smallest.

5.23   5.31   5.3   5.28   4.67   4.7

2 Use a calculator to work these out.

a 37p × 74   b 7 @ £12.60 each   c 4.75 m × 8

d (5 + 7) × 16   e (4.7 − 3.3) × (2.6 + 5.9)   f 6 × (3.8)²

g $\dfrac{25}{12 - 7}$ h $\dfrac{12.5 + 6.6}{12.9 - 10.4}$ i $\dfrac{15^2}{0.625 \times 8}$

3 Work out whether **A** or **B** is the correct answer to each of these.

a £140 ÷ 25 =   **A** £5.06   **B** £5.60

b £951 ÷ 50 =   **A** £19.20   **B** £19.02

c 18 minutes ÷ 12 =   **A** 1 minute 50 seconds   **B** 1 minute 30 seconds

d 12 minutes ÷ 5 =   **A** 2 minute 24 seconds   **B** 2 minute 40 seconds

4 Use the sign change key to help with these calculations.

a 48 ÷ −5 × 67   b 26 + −6 × 41

c 63 − −8 + 7²   d 567 ÷ (−9)²

5 Interpret these metric measures in the units given.

a 13.6 kg in kg and g   b 1.2 km in km and m

c 4.75 l in l and ml   d 3.8 cm in cm and mm

e 4.05 kg in kg and g   f 25.45 m in m and cm

6 Use a calculator to work these out. Remember to write the units with your answer.

a A loaf of bread weighs 770 g. How much do five loaves weigh?
   Give your answer in kg.

b A chocolate bar 20 cm long is divided into three equal pieces.
   How long is each piece?

c Lucy buys three tins of cat food. Each tin weighs 415 g.
   She shares the food between her six cats.
   What weight of food does each cat get?

7 Use the brackets or memory keys on your calculator to work these out.
   You will need to use BIDMAS.

a (18.92 ÷ 2.2) + (13.6 × 1.2)   b $\sqrt{15.68 \times 2} + 23.5^2$

c (4.55 + 12.45)² − 229.5 ÷ 2.55   d $\dfrac{18.9}{\sqrt{40.5 \div 4.5}} - 0.5^2$

10.1 Position-to-term rules

1 This is a CCC (Calculator Challenge Curve). Copy the curve.
Start at the first calculation and use a calculator to fill in the missing values.

$4914 \div 273 = \bigcirc \times 47 = \bigcirc - 366 = \bigcirc \div 96 = \bigcirc \times 187 = \bigcirc + 65 = \bigcirc$

2 Copy and complete the tables.

a

Position in sequence	1	2	3	4	5
Sequence	5	10	15		

   i Find the 10th term in this sequence.
   ii Find the 20th term in this sequence.

b

Position in sequence	1	2	3	4	5
Sequence	5	7	9		

   i Find the 10th term in this sequence.
   ii Find the 30th term in this sequence.

3 For each of these sequences, write down the 1st, 10th and 50th terms.
   a nth term is $n + 10$ **b** nth term is $n \times 5$
   c nth term is $n \div 2$ **d** nth term is $6n - 6$

4 a Copy and complete this table.

nth term	First five terms of the sequence	Term-to-term rule
$2n + 5$		
$3n + 4$		
$4n - 3$		

   b What is the connection between the nth term rule and the term-to-term rule?

5 Write down the first five terms of each of these sequences.
   a nth term is $n - 10$ **b** nth term is $6 - n$
   c nth term is $n \div 2 - 5$ **d** nth term is $6 - 6n$

6 For each of these sequences, write down the 10th and 50th terms.
   a nth term is $n - 10$ **b** nth term is $6 - n$
   c nth term is $n \div 2 - 5$ **d** nth term is $6 - 6n$

7 a Copy and complete this table.

nth term	First five terms of the sequence	Term-to-term rule
$3n - 10$		
$100 - 5n$		
$-3 - 4n$		

   b What is the connection between the nth term rule and the term-to-term rule?

10.2 Describing the nth term

1 Use a mental method to work out: **a** 3 × 0.3   **b** 6 × 0.4

2 On a local road, Abi notices that there are 20 lampposts every kilometre.
If she walks 2 km, she will walk past:

  2 × 20 = 40 lampposts.

  a How many lampposts will she walk past if she walks 5 km?

  b Copy and complete these formulae for how many lampposts Abi will walk past.

   i number of lampposts (L) = number of kilometres (n) × ____

   ii L = n × ____

  c How far has Abi walked if she passes 140 lampposts?

3 Look at this number sequence.

Position (n)	1	2	3	4	5
Term (T)	4	8	12	16	20

  a Write down the term-to-term rule.

  b Describe in words the position-to-term rule.

  c Write the position-to-term rule using algebra.

4 Look at this number sequence.

Position (n)	1	2	3	4	5
Term (T)	9	18	27	36	45

What is the 11th term of this sequence? Explain how you worked out your answer.

5 Look at this number sequence.

Position (n)	1	2	3	4	5
Term (T)	8	11	14	17	20

  a Write down the term-to-term rule.

  b Describe in words the position-to-term rule.

  c Write the position-to-term rule using algebra.

6 This sequence of squares is made from dots.

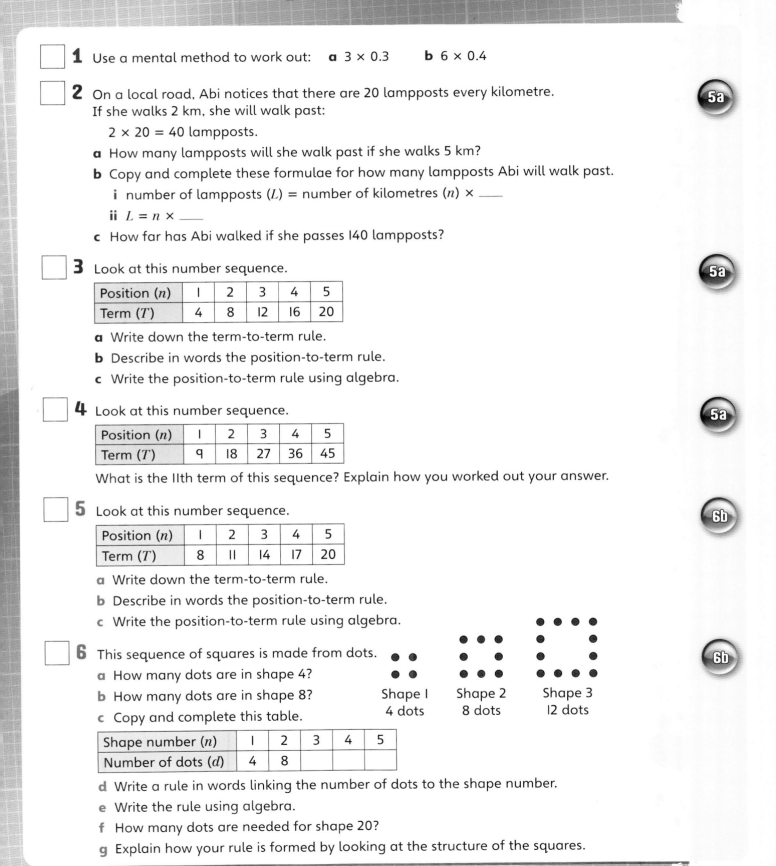

Shape 1
4 dots

Shape 2
8 dots

Shape 3
12 dots

  a How many dots are in shape 4?

  b How many dots are in shape 8?

  c Copy and complete this table.

Shape number (n)	1	2	3	4	5
Number of dots (d)	4	8			

  d Write a rule in words linking the number of dots to the shape number.

  e Write the rule using algebra.

  f How many dots are needed for shape 20?

  g Explain how your rule is formed by looking at the structure of the squares.

10.3 Functions and mappings

1 In the shape below, the numbers in the two circles multiply together to give the number in the square between them. Copy and complete.

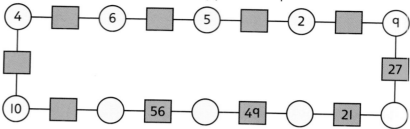

2 Write down the missing outputs for this function machine.

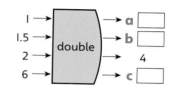

 4a

3 This function machine can be used to generate multiples of 10.

Input ⟶ ×10 ⟶ Output

What will the output value be when the input value is:

a 5?　　　　**b** 9?　　　　**c** 15?　　　　**d** 357?

 4a

4 Copy and complete this function machine. Find the missing inputs and outputs.

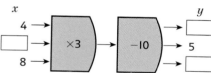

 5c

5 a Find the missing rule for this function machine.

b What is the output when the input is 3?

c What is the input when the output is 85?

 5b

6 Express the function machine in Q4 as a function.

$y =$ _____

 6c

7 a Copy these number lines.

b Draw a mapping diagram for the function $y = 3x - 5$

6b

10.4 Coordinates and straight-line graphs 1

1 The numbers on the yellow cards have been rounded to the nearest 100 to give the numbers on the pink cards.

245   1589   2200   250   2000   300

2100   200   1950   1600   2057

   a Match each yellow card with the correct pink card.

   b Which pink card is left over?

2 Look at the shape on this coordinate grid.
Copy and complete the coordinates of the
points on the corners of the shape.
   A (2, ___)   B (___, 6)   C (___, ...)   D (___, ...)

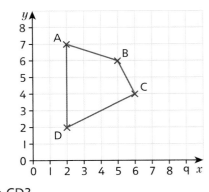

4c

3 Copy the coordinate grid in Q2.

   a What are the coordinates of the midpoint of the side CD?

   b Extend the lines AB and DC until they cross.
What are the coordinates of the point where the two lines cross?

   c Extend the line CD until it crosses the y-axis.
What are the coordinates of the point where the line crosses the y-axis?

4b

4 **a** Draw an x- and y-axis from 0 to 8.

   b Plot these coordinates. Join them with a straight line in the order they are given.
     (8, 0) (2, 2) (2, 7) (8, 5) (8, 0)

   c What shape have you drawn?

4a

5 **a** Copy and complete this table of values for the rule $y = 2x$.

x	I		3		5
y		4		8	

   b Copy and complete the coordinate pairs from your table.
     (I, ___) (___, 4) (3, ___) (___, 8) (5, ___)

5a

6 **a** Copy and complete this table of values for the rule
$y = 2x + 2$.

x	I	2	3		
y				10	12

   b Copy and complete the coordinate pairs from your table.
     (I, ___) (2, ___) (3, ___) (___, 10) (___, 12)

5a

7 **a** On graph paper draw a pair of axes, with the x-axis
between 0 and 5 and the y-axis between 0 and 14.

   b Plot the graphs of Q5 and 6 on the same grid.

   c Copy and complete this sentence.
The graphs of $y = 2x$ and $y = 2x + 2$ are _____

5a

10.5 Coordinates and straight-line graphs 2

1 Put these cards into groups of three equivalent cards.
Each group must contain one pink, one yellow and one blue card.

| 23% | $\frac{9}{100}$ | 0.17 | $\frac{1}{10}$ | 0.9 | $\frac{17}{100}$ | 9% | 0.23 |
| $\frac{9}{10}$ | 10% | 0.09 | 17% | 0.1 | $\frac{23}{100}$ | 90% |

2 Look at the coordinate axes.
The line AD has the rule: $x = -4$
Copy and complete these sentences:
a The line AB has the rule: $y = $ ____
b The line BC has the rule: _____
c The line CD has the rule: _____

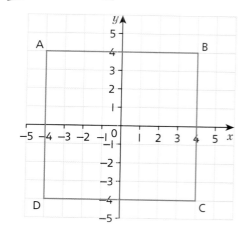

5b

3 a Make a copy of the coordinate axes in Q2.
b Plot these points. Join them with a straight line in the order they are given.
$(-3, 3)$ $(3, 3)$ $(3, -3)$ $(-3, -3)$ $(-3, 2)$ $(2, 2)$ $(2, -2)$
$(-2, -2)$ $(-2, 1)$ $(1, 1)$ $(1, -1)$ $(-1, -1)$ $(-1, 0)$ $(0, 0)$

5a

4 The rule $y = x + 2$ can be written as the function machine
When $x = 4$, $y = 4 + 2 = 6$. The coordinate pair is $(4, 6)$
Find the coordinate pair when

$x \rightarrow \boxed{+2} \rightarrow y$

a $x = 5$ **b** $x = 0$ **c** $x = -5$

6c

5 a Which rule can be written as this function machine?

$x \rightarrow \boxed{\times 3} \rightarrow \boxed{+1} \rightarrow y$

b Copy and complete this table of values for the rule in part **a**.

x	1	2	3	4	
y					31

6c

6 a On graph paper draw a pair of axes, with the x-axis between -5 and 5 and
the y-axis between -10 and 10.
b Plot the graphs of: **i** $y = x + 2$ **ii** $y = 3x - 2$
c Write down the coordinates of the point where the two graphs cross.

6b

Play any game on the LiveText CD.

11.1 Accurate angles

1 Convert these percentages to fractions.

a $7\% = \dfrac{\square}{100}$
b $23\% = \dfrac{\square}{100}$
c $10\% = \dfrac{\square}{100} = \dfrac{\square}{10}$
d $90\% = \dfrac{\square}{10}$

2 a Measure the angles inside each of these shapes.

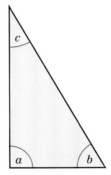 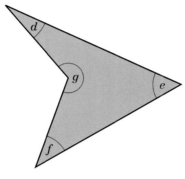

b For each shape, find the total of the inside (interior) angles.

3 Draw these angles accurately using a protractor.
Write down next to each angle whether it is acute or obtuse.

a 160°
b 16°
c 100°

4 Draw the reflex angle 300° accurately using a protractor.

5 Construct this SAS triangle accurately using a ruler and protractor.

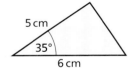

6 Construct this ASA triangle accurately using a ruler and protractor.

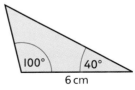

7 Two bees leave different flowers 120 m apart, as shown in the sketch.
They fly to the same beehive in a direct line.
Make a scale drawing using a scale of 1 cm = 10 m, and use it to find out how far each bee has to fly to get to the beehive.

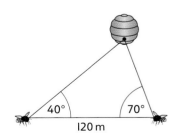

11.2 More constructions

1 Copy and complete this number puzzle.

	×	5	=	30		
		×		÷		
		4	×		=	
÷		=		=		×
9			−	10	=	
=						=
	×	6	=	48		

2 a Construct triangle ABC where AB is the base and is 4 cm, AC is 6 cm and ∠CAB = 120°.

  b Measure the length of BC.

  c Measure the size of ∠ABC.

3 a Use a ruler and compasses to draw an accurate diagram of this triangle.

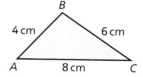

  b Measure the size of ∠ABC.

4 a Accurately draw this diagram.

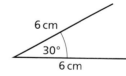

  b Use a ruler and compasses to construct the angle bisector. Make sure you show your construction lines.

5 Draw a horizontal line 10 cm long.
Use compasses to draw the perpendicular bisector.
Make sure you show your construction lines.

6 a Use compasses to accurately draw this triangle.

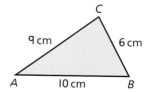

  b Use construction skills to find the shortest distance from point C to the line AB. Make sure you show your construction lines.

  c How long is the line from C to AB?

11.3 Blake Hunter

1 Round £4,649 to the nearest: **a** £100   **b** £1000

2 Blake has nine different designs of panes of glass.

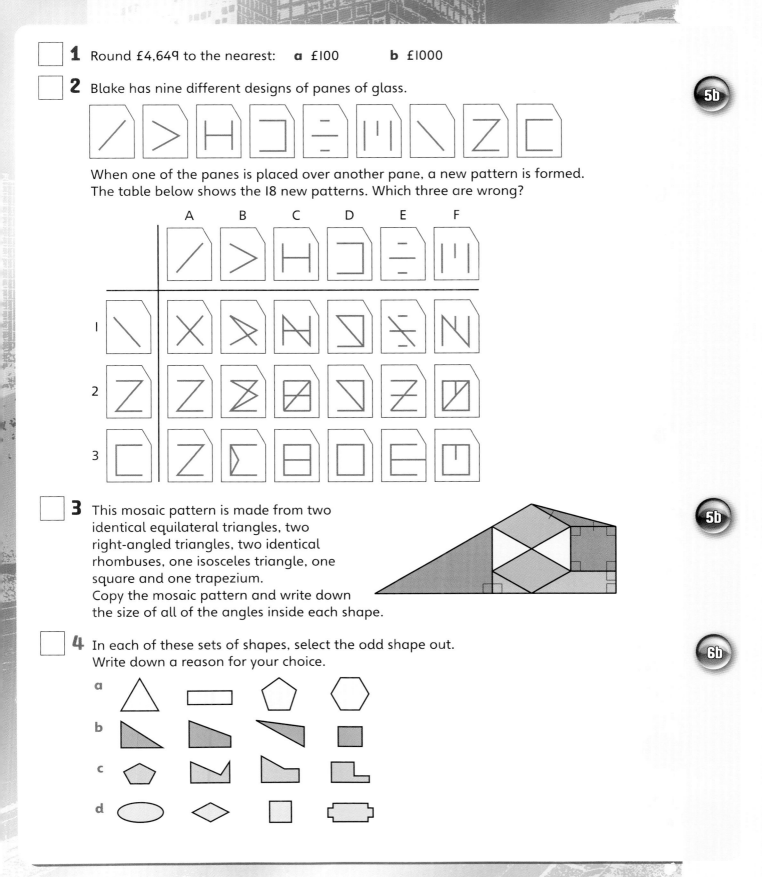

When one of the panes is placed over another pane, a new pattern is formed.
The table below shows the 18 new patterns. Which three are wrong?

3 This mosaic pattern is made from two
identical equilateral triangles, two
right-angled triangles, two identical
rhombuses, one isosceles triangle, one
square and one trapezium.
Copy the mosaic pattern and write down
the size of all of the angles inside each shape.

4 In each of these sets of shapes, select the odd shape out.
Write down a reason for your choice.

a

b

c

d

11.4 Geometry in practice

1 For each part, write down which fraction is **not** equivalent to the other two.

a $\frac{1}{2}, \frac{3}{8}, \frac{6}{12}$ b $\frac{2}{3}, \frac{6}{9}, \frac{8}{15}$ c $\frac{2}{5}, \frac{3}{4}, \frac{12}{16}$ d $\frac{4}{5}, \frac{16}{25}, \frac{24}{30}$

2 Find the missing angles a, b, c, d, e and f.

a 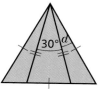   b   c

d 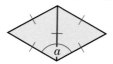   e 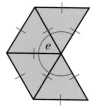   f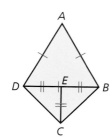

 5a

3 a Calculate angle a in this triangle.

b How many of these angles are needed to add up to 360°?

c How many sides does a polygon have, if it is made using the same triangle with angle a at the centre?

 6c

4 The quadrilateral ABCD is made from three triangles.
Triangle ABD is equilateral.
Triangles BCE and CDE are identical isosceles triangles.
Work out the size of ∠ABC.

 6c

5 Find the missing angles marked with letters in this diagram.

 6a

6 Find the missing angles marked with letters in this diagram.

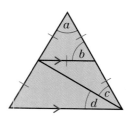

 6a

11.5 Bearings

1 Use the column method to work out these additions.

   a 4592 + 3927   **b** 13486 + 27819   **b** 382 + 916 + 478

2 What bearing is the same as 'north west'?

3 a What is the bearing from A to B?

   b What is the bearing from B to A?

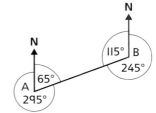

4 Copy and complete this table using the map to help you.
Choose a bearing from the list:

   005°   138°   085°   324°

   106°   022°   175°   242°

   198°   352°   258°   280°

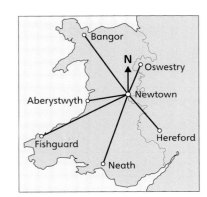

Town	Bearing from Newtown
Oswestry	
Hereford	
Neath	
Fishguard	
Aberystwyth	
Bangor	

5 Copy this map onto squared paper.
Measure the bearing of:

   a town B from town F

   b town B from town S

   c town F from town S

   d town S from town B.

6 On a boat-handling course, Kim was given these instructions.
Go 1500 m on a bearing of 120°, then travel true north for 500 m.

   a Make a scale drawing of Kim's journey. Use a scale of 1 cm to represent 100 m.

   b In a straight line, how far is Kim from her starting point?

   c On what bearing must Kim travel to get back to her starting point?

12.1 Percentages

1 **a** Use an approximate calculation to work out which two of the following are wrong.
  i $502 \times 6 = 1506$ **ii** $212 \times 9 = 1908$ **iii** $783 \times 4 = 1566$

  b For the two that are wrong, work out the correct answers.

2 A box of cereal has this list of ingredients.

> **Ingredients**
> Rice (60%), Wheat (20%), Sugar (5%),
> Barley malt extract, Dried skimmed
> milk, Niacin, Vitamin E, Folic acid, Iron

The box of cereal holds 500 g.
How many grams of the box of cereal are:

  a rice?   **b** wheat?   **c** sugar?

3 Convert these percentages to fractions:

  a with denominator 100
   i 12% **ii** 57% **iii** 9% **iv** 73%

  b with denominator 10
   i 20% **ii** 70% **iii** 90% **iv** 180%

4 This table shows the amount that four children earn and the amount that they save.

	Amount earned	Amount saved
Alice	£40	£20
Joe	£30	£10
Isobel	£35	£25
Carlos	£32	£24

Write the amount they save as a fraction of the amount they earn.
Simplify your fractions.

5 Rewrite these statements giving the numbers as percentages.
Convert to an equivalent fraction with denominator 100.

  a 8 out of 20 women like to watch rugby.

  b 15 out of 25 men like to watch cricket.

  c 4 out of 5 children support a football team.

  d 24 out of 48 adults go for a walk every day.

6 Nadia is making a cake.
She uses 200 g out of a 1 kg bag of flour.
What fraction of the bag of flour has she used?
Give your answer in its simplest form.

7 Express the first amount as a fraction of the second amount.
Give your answer in its simplest form.

  a 40p and £1.60   **b** 5 mm and 6 cm

  c 25 seconds and 1 minute   **d** 18 hours and 1 day

4c

4b

5b

5a

6b

6b

12.2 Ratio

1 Work out these exact divisions.

a 496 ÷ 4   b 582 ÷ 6   c 963 ÷ 9   d 930 ÷ 5

2 Shen makes a light blue paint by mixing dark blue paint with white paint.
He uses 1 can of dark blue paint for every 2 cans of white paint.
If there are 12 cans altogether, how many of the cans are

a dark blue paint?   b white paint?

3 Andre makes a crème caramel using milk, cream, sugar and eggs.
For every 8 ml of milk he uses 5 ml of cream.

milk

cream

The recipe needs a **total** of 650 ml of milk and cream mixed together.

a How many ml of milk does Andre use?

b How many ml of cream does Andre use?

4 Dave and Caroline win lots of prizes.
They share the prize money they win using ratio notation.
How much do they each get if they win:

a £200 and share it in the ratio 2:3?

b £450 and share it in the ratio 5:4?

c £630 and share it in the ratio 4:3?

5 Find these fractions and percentages.

a The ratio of white eggs to brown eggs produced on
a farm is 1:3.
What percentage of the eggs are brown?

b The ratio of girls to boys in a class is 2:3.
What percentage of the class are girls?

c The ratio of white to milk chocolates in a box is 3:5.
What fraction of the box are milk chocolates?

d The ratio of customers to staff on a horse riding trek is 7:2.
What fraction of the people on the trek are customers?

6 A box contains toffee, truffle and nut centred chocolates in the ratio 1:3:2.
There are 30 chocolates in the box.
How many of the chocolates have a:

a toffee centre   b truffle centre   c nut centre?

7 A grandfather leaves £3 000 in his will to his three grandchildren in the ratio 2:5:8.
How much does each grandchild receive?

12.3 Proportion

1 **a** Write down the numbers from the pentagon that are square numbers.

b **i** Write down the numbers from the pentagon that aren't square numbers.
   ii Add these numbers together.
   iii Is this total a square number?

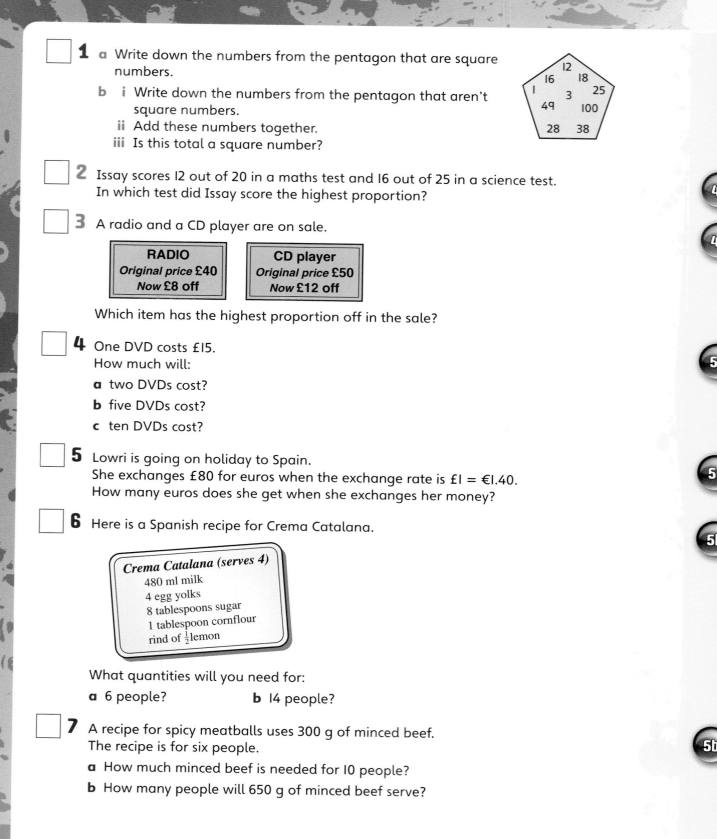

Pentagon: 12, 16, 18, 1, 3, 25, 49, 100, 28, 38

2 Issay scores 12 out of 20 in a maths test and 16 out of 25 in a science test. In which test did Issay score the highest proportion?

3 A radio and a CD player are on sale.

RADIO	CD player
Original price £40	Original price £50
Now £8 off	Now £12 off

Which item has the highest proportion off in the sale?

4 One DVD costs £15.
How much will:

a two DVDs cost?

b five DVDs cost?

c ten DVDs cost?

5 Lowri is going on holiday to Spain.
She exchanges £80 for euros when the exchange rate is £1 = €1.40.
How many euros does she get when she exchanges her money?

6 Here is a Spanish recipe for Crema Catalana.

Crema Catalana (serves 4)
480 ml milk
4 egg yolks
8 tablespoons sugar
1 tablespoon cornflour
rind of $\frac{1}{2}$ lemon

What quantities will you need for:

a 6 people?   **b** 14 people?

7 A recipe for spicy meatballs uses 300 g of minced beef.
The recipe is for six people.

a How much minced beef is needed for 10 people?

b How many people will 650 g of minced beef serve?

4a 4a 5c 5c 5b 5b

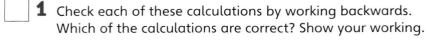

12.4 More ratio and proportion

1 Check each of these calculations by working backwards.
Which of the calculations are correct? Show your working.

    a $3572 + 2189 = 5671$ **b** $439 \times 6 = 2634$

    c $834 \div 3 = 278$ **d** $4497 - 1856 = 2641$

2 The stars show some percentages
and their equivalent decimals.
Match the percentages with
their equivalent decimals.

3 Copy and complete this table.

Percentage	Fraction	Decimal
10%		
	$\frac{2}{5}$	
		0.16
35%		
	$\frac{7}{50}$	
		1.75

4 In class 7A, 12 out of the 25 pupils have a pet dog.
In class 7B, 45% of pupils have a pet dog.
Which class has the greater proportion of pupils with a pet dog?

5 A fruit punch is made using 200 ml of orange juice, 100 ml of apple juice and 300 ml of
ginger ale.

    a What fraction of the fruit punch is ginger ale?

    b What is the ratio of orange juice to apple juice to ginger ale?

6 A group of adults were asked what they usually had for breakfast.
One fifth had porridge, 38% had cereal and the rest had toast.
Which breakfast was the most popular?

7 This is the sandwich menu in a cafe.

On one day 15% of the customers
buy cheese and pickle sandwiches.
$\frac{1}{8}$ of the customers buy ham and
tomato sandwiches.
Which of the sandwiches has the
greater proportion of sales and by how much?

SANDWICHES
Cheese and pickle
Ham and tomato

12.5 Solving ratio and proportion problems

1 This is a CCC (Calculator Challenge Curve). Copy the curve.
Start at the first calculation and use a calculator to fill in the missing values.

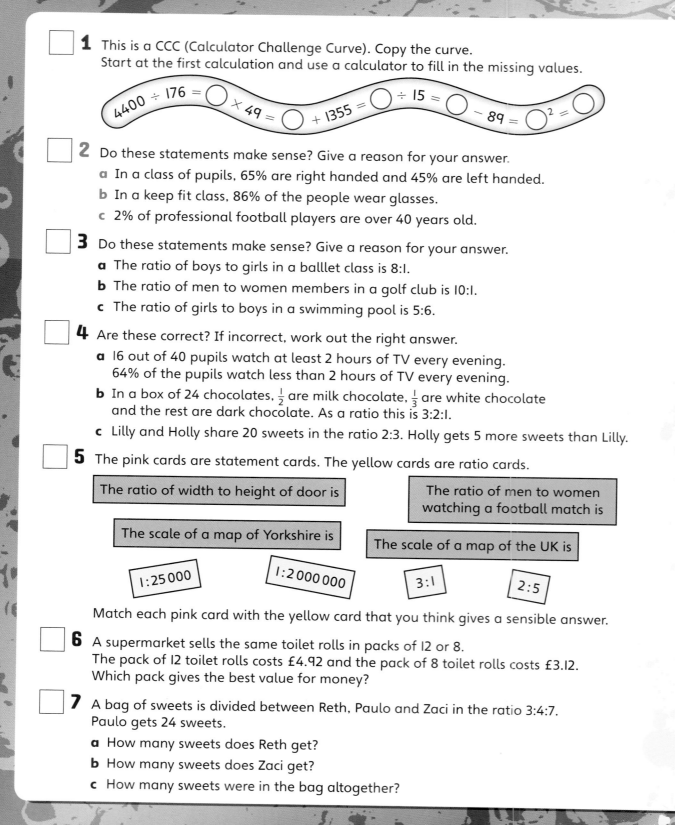

4400 ÷ 176 = ◯ × 49 = ◯ + 1355 = ◯ ÷ 15 = ◯ − 89 = ◯² = ◯

2 Do these statements make sense? Give a reason for your answer.

　a In a class of pupils, 65% are right handed and 45% are left handed.

　b In a keep fit class, 86% of the people wear glasses.

　c 2% of professional football players are over 40 years old.

3 Do these statements make sense? Give a reason for your answer.

　a The ratio of boys to girls in a balllet class is 8:1.

　b The ratio of men to women members in a golf club is 10:1.

　c The ratio of girls to boys in a swimming pool is 5:6.

4 Are these correct? If incorrect, work out the right answer.

　a 16 out of 40 pupils watch at least 2 hours of TV every evening.
　　64% of the pupils watch less than 2 hours of TV every evening.

　b In a box of 24 chocolates, $\frac{1}{2}$ are milk chocolate, $\frac{1}{3}$ are white chocolate
　　and the rest are dark chocolate. As a ratio this is 3:2:1.

　c Lilly and Holly share 20 sweets in the ratio 2:3. Holly gets 5 more sweets than Lilly.

5 The pink cards are statement cards. The yellow cards are ratio cards.

| The ratio of width to height of door is | | The ratio of men to women watching a football match is |

| The scale of a map of Yorkshire is | | The scale of a map of the UK is |

| 1:25 000 | 1:2 000 000 | 3:1 | 2:5 |

Match each pink card with the yellow card that you think gives a sensible answer.

6 A supermarket sells the same toilet rolls in packs of 12 or 8.
The pack of 12 toilet rolls costs £4.92 and the pack of 8 toilet rolls costs £3.12.
Which pack gives the best value for money?

7 A bag of sweets is divided between Reth, Paulo and Zaci in the ratio 3:4:7.
Paulo gets 24 sweets.

　a How many sweets does Reth get?

　b How many sweets does Zaci get?

　c How many sweets were in the bag altogether?

4b
5c
5c
5c
5a
5a

13.1 Solving simple equations

1 Copy and complete this number pyramid.
Find each missing number by multiplying the two bricks below it.

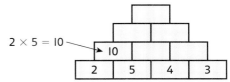

$2 \times 5 = 10$

2 a Put these cards into pairs with the same answer.
  b Which card is the odd one out?

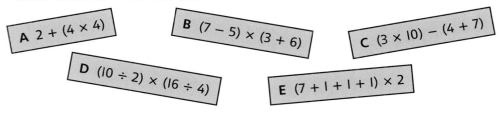

A $2 + (4 \times 4)$

B $(7 - 5) \times (3 + 6)$

C $(3 \times 10) - (4 + 7)$

D $(10 \div 2) \times (16 \div 4)$

E $(7 + 1 + 1 + 1) \times 2$

3 Work out: $5^2 + 4(3 - 2)$

4 Put the numbers 2, 3, 4 and 5 in the boxes to make the following true.

$(\boxed{} + \boxed{}) + (\boxed{} \times \boxed{}) = 19$

5 Write down **true** or **false** for each of these.
  a $4a = a \times 4$ **b** $b^2 = b \times b$
  c $ce = c + e$ **d** $3d = d + d + d$

6 Solve these equations.
  a $3 \times n = 15$ **b** $5n = 15$
  c $x + 4 = 15$ **d** $\frac{x}{2} = 15$
  e $6 + x = 15$ **f** $6 - x = 15$

7 Solve these equations by using inverse operations.
  a $4x + 3 = 15$ **b** $3x - 6 = 15$
  c $\frac{x}{3} + 5 = 15$ **d** $\frac{x}{5} - 3 = 15$

13.2 Solving more complex equations

1 Round these numbers to the nearest 10.

a 68   b 72   c 185   d 6798

2 Do you speak maths?

Translate each of these English descriptions into maths expressions.
For example: 'the mystery number add three' translates to $x + 3$.

a The mystery number divided by six.

b Seven divided by the mystery number.

c The mystery number multiplied by six then added to one.

d The mystery number multiplied by itself and subtracted from ten.

3 Multiply out the expressions

a $4(x + 3)$ b $5(4x - 3)$ c $6(5 - 4x)$

4 a Solve the equations on these cards.

A $4n - 3 = 17$ B $2n + 5 = 17$ C $3n + 2 = 17$

b Which card is the odd one out?

5 Solve each of the following.

a "I think of a number, I multiply by two and add six.
The answer is 20.
What is the number I thought of?"

b The perimeter of this rectangle is 34 cm.
What is the value of n?

c $3(2x - 4) = 24$

2n + 1 cm

4 cm   4 cm

2n + 1 cm

6 a Construct an equation involving the
short sides of this rectangle.

b Solve the equation to find the value of a.

c Construct an equation involving the long sides
of this rectangle.

d Solve the equation to find the value of b.

e What is the perimeter of the rectangle?

← 4b + 1 cm →

2a + 4 cm   3a − 6 cm

← 5b − 8 cm →

7 The area of this rectangle is 120 cm².

5 cm

5x + 4 cm

a Write an equation for the area of the rectangle.

b Solve the equation to find the value of x.

13.3 Constructing and solving equations

1 Work these out without using a calculator.

    a $6 + 4 \times 2$ **b** $20 - 18 \div 2$ **c** $15 \div 5 + 7$ **d** $3 \times 5 - 2 \times 4$

2 Look at this triangle.

    a Use the fact that there are 180° in a triangle to write down an equation.

    b Solve the equation to find the value of angle a.

    c Write down the size of the largest angle.

3 Look at this triangle.
The perimeter of the triangle is 30 cm.

    a Write down an equation for the perimeter.

    b Solve the equation to find the value of b.

    c Write down the length of each side of the triangle.

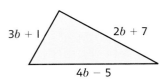

4 There are 180 passengers altogether on three trains.
There are n passengers on the first train.
There are twice as many passengers on the second train as there are on the first train.
There are 20 more passengers on the third train as there are on the first train.

    a Write down an expression for the number of passengers on the second train.

    b Write down an expression for the number of passengers on the third train.

    c Write down an equation for the total number of passengers on the three trains.

    d Solve the equation to find the value of n.

    e Write down how many passengers there are on each train.

5 Solve these equations.

    a $3x = 5 + 2x$ **b** $3x = x + 8$ **c** $8x - 4 = 6 + 3x$

    d $3(2x - 1) = 4x + 10$ **e** $3(5x + 4) = x + 4(x - 2)$

6 Here are a rectangle and a square.

    a Write an expression for the perimeter of each shape.

    b The shapes have the same perimeter.
Write an equation using your expressions in part **a**.

    c Solve the equation to find the value of x.

    d What is the side length of the square?

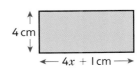

7 A mystery number n is added to 4.
The result is multiplied by 3.
The answer is the same as 5 times the mystery number, then minus 4.

    a Write an equation for this mystery number problem.

    b Solve the equation to find the mystery number.

6c 6c 6c 6b 6b 6b

Play any game on the LiveText CD.

13.4 Equation quest

1 A tin of chilli baked beans has this list of ingredients.

> **Ingredients**
> Beans (50%), Tomatoes (30%), Water,
> Red peppers (5%), Onions, Sugar,
> Modified cornflour, Salt, Spirit vinegar,
> Garlic Puree, Spices, Sweetener.

The tin holds 400 g of chilli baked beans.
How many grams are:

a beans   **b** tomatoes   **c** red peppers?

2 The perimeter of each of these shapes is 56 cm.
For each shape, form an equation and solve it to find the lengths of the unknown sides.

a   **b** 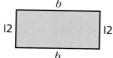   **c**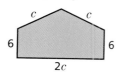

3 In this rectangle all the sides are measured in cm.

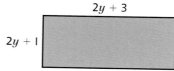

a Find the lengths of the shorter sides.
b Find the lengths of the longer sides.
c Find the perimeter of the rectangle.
d Find the area of the rectangle.

4 In this rectangle all the sides are measured in mm.

$2y + 3$

$2y + 1$

Sabrina knows that 3 × the longer side is the same length as 5 × the shorter side
Use this information to

a form an equation
b find the length of the shorter side
c find the length of the longer side
d work out the perimeter of the rectangle
e work out the area of the rectangle.

14.1 Translation and reflection

1 Without using a calculator, find the value of these.

    a $2 \times (6 + 3)$ **b** $(12 - 8) \times 5$ **c** $27 \div (12 - 3)$ **d** $(9 - 3) \times (4 + 5)$

2 In each of these diagrams decide whether the lines drawn are lines of reflection. Write **yes** or **no**.

    a   **b**   **c**   **d**

  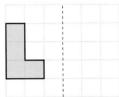 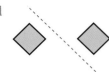

3 Copy this L shape onto squared paper.
Draw the reflection of the shape in the dotted mirror line.

4 Copy this T shape onto squared paper.
Translate the shape 3 squares right and 2 up.

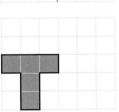

5 I translate a shape 4 right and 2 up. Then I translate the image 4 right and 4 down. What single translation has the same effect as these two translations combined?

6 Copy this diagram.

    a Reflect the shape in the line $y = x$.

    b Reflect the shape in the line $x = -1$

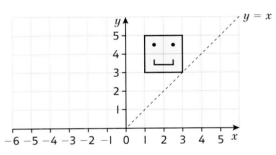

7 Copy this coordinate grid and rectangle A.

    a Reflect A in the line $y = x$.
       Label the image B.

    b Reflect A in the line $y = -x$.
       Label the image C.

    c Describe the reflection you must carry out on rectangle C to complete the pattern of rectangles so that the pattern has two lines of symmetry.

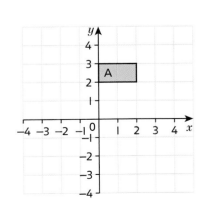

14.2 Rotation

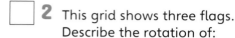

1 Use a mental method to work these out.

    a 8×0.8 **b** 4×0.4 **c** 0.02×2

    d $8 \times 0.8 + 4 \times 0.4 + 0.02 \times 2$

2 This grid shows three flags.
Describe the rotation of:

    a A onto B

    b C onto A.

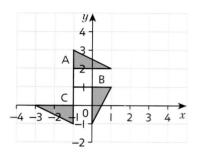

3 A shape has coordinates
(0, 1) (2, 1) (3, 1) (3, −1) and (2, −1).
Write down the coordinates of the
shape after a rotation of:

    a 90° anticlockwise about (0, 1)

    b 180° about (0, 1).

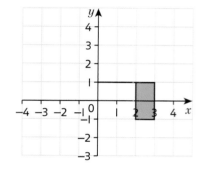

4 Describe the transformation of:

    a the pink shape to the orange shape

    b the pink shape to the blue shape

    c the orange shape to the blue shape

    d the blue shape to the red shape

    e the orange shape to the green shape

    f the red shape to the green shape.

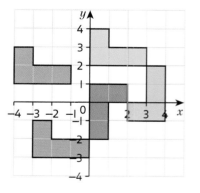

5 This regular pentagon is formed
by five isosceles triangles.
Describe fully the rotation of:

    a OAB onto OBC

    b OAB onto OCD

    c ODE onto OBC.

6 A rectangle has coordinates
(0, 0) (a, 0) (a, b) and (0, b).
Write down the coordinates of the
rectangle after a rotation about (0, 0) of:

    a 90° clockwise   **b** 180°.

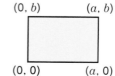

14.3 Symmetry

1 This is a MCC (Mental Challenge Curve). Copy the curve.
Start at the first calculation, then mentally work out the missing values.

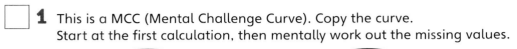

6 × 7 = ◯ + 18 = ◯ ÷ 10 = ◯ × 9 = ◯ − 22 = ◯ ÷ 8 = ◯² = ◯

2 Copy each shape and draw in any lines of symmetry.

a   b   c   d

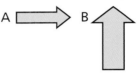 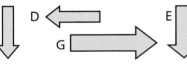 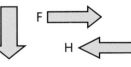

3 Write down the number of lines of symmetry and the order of rotational symmetry of each shape.

a   b   c   d

4 Write down which of these arrows are congruent to arrow **A**.

A ⇨   B ⇧   C ⇩   D ⇦   E ⇩   F ⇨   G ⇨   H ⇦

5 a Copy this diagram.

b Shade two more squares to
make a pattern with order of
rotational symmetry 2.

c Write down the number of lines
of symmetry of your pattern.

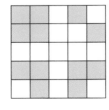

6 This is a parallelogram.

a How many lines of symmetry does the parallelogram have?

b What is the order of rotational symmetry of the parallelogram?

c Sketch the parallelogram and show how it can be split into:

i two congruent triangles   ii two congruent quadrilaterals.

7 I have a shape whose object and image after any number of turns of 45° are identical.
Work out the order of rotational symmetry of the shape.

5c
5c
5c
6c
6c
6b

14.4 Combining transformations

1 Copy and complete these multiplications using the grid method.

a 328 × 4

×	300	20	8
4			

b 276 × 3

×	200	70	6
3			

2 Here are three rectangles.
Copy and complete these sentences
that describe the transformation of:

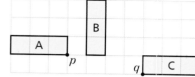

a rectangle A to rectangle B
A rotation of ...° clockwise about ... followed by a translation of ... square right.

b rectangle C to rectangle B
A rotation of ...° .... about ... followed by a translation of ... squares left
and ... square up.

3 Here are three shapes.

a Describe the reflection of the pink shape to
the red shape.

b Describe the reflection of the pink shape to
the blue shape.

c Write down a single transformation that
transforms the red shape to the blue shape.

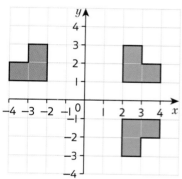

4 a Copy this diagram and reflect the triangle in
the line $x = 1$.

b Reflect the image in the line $y = 2$.

c Describe a single transformation which is
equivalent to these two reflections combined.

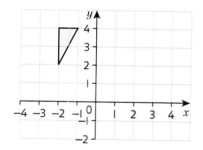

5 Look at this diagram.

a Describe the translation that transforms the
blue shape to the orange shape.

b Describe the reflection that transforms the
blue shape to the yellow shape.

c Describe the rotation that transforms the
blue shape to the green shape.

d Describe a rotation and a translation that
transform the blue shape to the red shape.

e Describe a reflection and a translation that
transform the green shape to the orange shape.

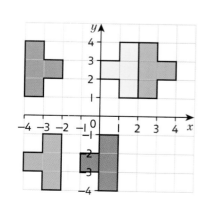

14.5 Enlargement

1 Write these temperatures in order of size, coldest first.

11°C   −3°C   −9°C   8°C   1°C   −1°C   −12°C

2 a Copy these shapes onto squared paper.
  b Enlarge shape A by multiplying all lengths by 2.
  c Enlarge shape B by multiplying all lengths by 3.

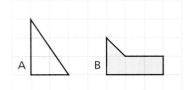

3 a Copy this shape onto squared paper.
  b Enlarge the shape by a scale factor of 4.

4 In this diagram the blue square has been enlarged to make the red square.
  a Write down the scale factor of the enlargement.
  b Copy the diagram and mark with a cross where the centre of the enlargement is.

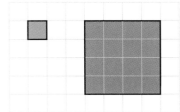

5 a Copy this shape onto squared paper.
  b Enlarge the shape by a scale factor of 2, using the red cross as the centre of enlargement.

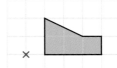

6 a Copy this diagram.
  b Enlarge shape A by a scale factor of 3, centre (2, 1)
  c Enlarge shape B by a scale factor of 2 centre (−5, 0)

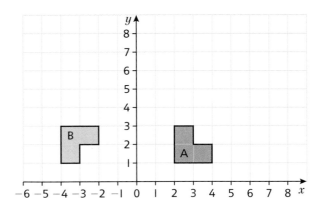

14.6 Problem solving

1 Use a calculator to work out $(12.95 - 7.86)^2 \times (0.004 + 0.35)$

2 A square tile has a perimeter of 32 cm.

   a Find the length of the side of the square.

   b Find the area of the square.

3 Here are a square and a rectangle.

 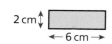

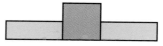

This shape is made from one square and two rectangles.

   a What is the area of this shape?

   b What is the perimeter of this shape?

4 This shape is made from four of the squares and four of the rectangles in Q3.

   a What is the outside perimeter of the shape?

   b What is the inside perimeter of the shape?

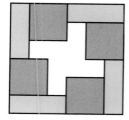

5 The total area of these three pink rectangles is the same as the area of the yellow rectangle.

   a Write an equation involving x.

   b Solve your equation to find x.

   c Find the area of the smallest rectangle.

6 This square has sides of length $2x$ cm.
It is cut into four congruent triangles.

   a Write down the base and height of one triangle.

   b Write down the area of one triangle.

7 This square has sides of length $2x$ cm.
It is cut into four congruent triangles.
Three of the triangles are made into a new shape.

   a Calculate the length of the new shape.

   b Calculate the area of the new shape.

 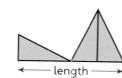

Play any game on the LiveText CD.

15.1 Finding averages

1 a Find the remainders for each of these divisions:
   i 428 ÷ 3   **ii** 704 ÷ 5   **iii** 793 ÷ 4

   b Find the total of the remainders found in part **a**.

   c Is this total a square number or a prime number?

2 This table shows the ages of the horses at a riding stable.

Age of horses	0–9	10–19	20–29	30–39
Frequency	8	23	12	2

   What is the modal class?

4a

3 There are nine boys in Jack's class.
   Their shoe sizes are 6, 4, 5, 4, 8, 10, 6, 11 and 6.
   Work out

   a the modal shoe size   **b** the range in shoe sizes.

4a

4 The ten judges in an ice-skating competition awarded an ice-skater these points:

   | 8.6 | 8.9 | 9.0 | 8.5 | 8.0 | 9.1 | 8.1 | 8.9 | 8.1 | 8.8 |

   Work out

   a the mean score   **b** the median score.

5c

5 This table shows the number of shots that 20 golfers took to complete the 1st hole on a golf course.

Number of shots taken	1	2	3	4	5
Frequency	1	3	9	5	2

   Work out

   a the modal number of shots

   b the mean number of shots

5c

6 Alicia travels to school by bus. She records the time it takes to get to school each day for a week. Here are her results.

   12 minutes, 12 minutes, 15 minutes, 18 minutes, 43 minutes

   What would be an appropriate average to use for this data?

6c

7 These are the times it takes a class of 20 pupils to run the 100 m sprint.

   | 14 s | 21 s | 16 s | 15 s | 17 s |

   | 19 s | 17 s | 19 s | 18 s | 15 s |

   | 16 s | 15 s | 14 s | 20 s | 17 s |

   | 15 s | 19 s | 18 s | 19 s | 16 s |

   Use an assumed mean of 16 seconds to find the mean time.

6b

15.2 Drawing and interpreting graphs

1 Copy and complete the following.

a $6 \times 8 = 48$ $48 \div \Box = 8$ $\Box \div 8 = 6$

b $4 \times \Box = 24$ $\Box \div 6 = 4$ $24 \div \Box = 6$

c $\Box \div 7 = 8$ $\Box \div 8 = 7$ $7 \times 8 = \Box$

2 Gareth asked his friends which rugby team they supported.
This table shows his results.

    a Copy and complete the table.

    b Draw a pie chart for this information.

Rugby team	Frequency	Number of degrees
Llanelli scarlets	8	
Cardiff blues	7	
Ospreys	5	
Totals	**20**	**360°**

3 Rhian asked her friends what their favourite hobby was.
This table shows her results.

    a Copy and complete the table.

    b Draw a pie chart for this information.

Hobby	Frequency	Number of degrees
Youth club	6	
Swimming	3	
Horse riding	4	
Rock climbing	2	
Totals		

4 Liam asked his friends which football team they supported.
Here are his results.

Football team	Frequency
Arsenal	6
West Ham	3
Chelsea	5
Charlton	2

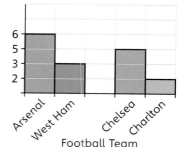

    a Write down four things that are wrong with his graph.

    b Draw a fully correct graph showing Liam's data.

5 a For each of these situations, choose the most appropriate graph to draw for

    i the proportions of boys and girls in a class

    ii the numbers of boys and girls in a class.

    iii the numbers of boys and girls in two classes.

Choose from: *line graph, dual-bar chart, pie chart, bar chart.*
Give reasons for your answers.

    b Which graph have you not used?
Describe a situation where you could use this graph.

15.3 Comparing distributions

1 Put the correct sign, > or <, between each pair of numbers.

  a 0.34 ☐ 0.25   **b** 0.06 ☐ 0.1   **c** 6.78 ☐ 6.7   **d** 120p ☐ £1.35

2 Alex and Javier carried out a survey on the way their friends travel to school. They both drew a bar chart of their results.

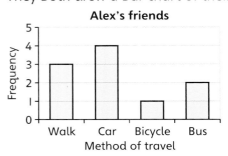 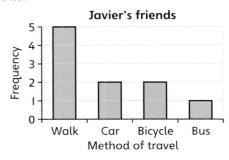

Use the mode to compare the way Alex's and Javier's friends travel to school.

3 Safara and Reth play a computer game. They try to get the highest score they can. They play the game nine times each. Here are their scores.

Safara	106	101	105	113	100	103	120	102	113
Reth	88	119	85	129	115	130	88	127	118

  a Work out the mean, median, mode and range for Safara and Reth.

  b Compare the values you found in part **a**, and decide who you think is the better player. Give reasons for your decision.

4 Fleur and Esta carried out a survey on the age of shoppers at a supermarket. One of them carried out their survey on a Saturday, the other on a Thursday. They each drew a graph to show the ages of the 30 people they asked.

 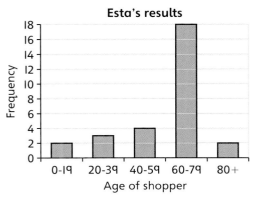

  a Compare and comment on the distribution of the ages of the shoppers that Fleur and Esta surveyed.

  b Which survey was carried out on a Saturday? Give a reason for your answer.

15.4 Reporting the facts

1 Without using a calculator find the value of these.

    a $3 \times (8 - 5)$ **b** $(15 + 5) \times 8$ **c** $12 \div (15 - 9)$ **d** $(8 + 3) \times (9 - 6)$

2 Ella's class are doing a project on the number of text messages they send.
Ella and two of her friends, Linda and Maria, keep a record of the number of texts they send over a bank holiday weekend.
The bar chart shows the results.

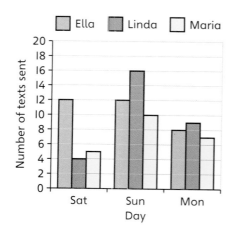

    a Write about the number of texts sent each day by the three friends.

    b It rained on one of the days.
       Which day do you think it was?
       Give a reason for your answer.

    c On one of the days, Linda and Maria met.
       Which day do you think it was?
       Give a reason for your answer.

3 Eight pupils in Ella's class regularly send texts. They all keep a record of how many texts they send during one week. The table shows the average number of texts each sends on a weekday and on a day at the weekend.

	Average number of texts sent on a weekday	Average number of texts sent on a day at the weekend
Ella	12.67	14.28
Linda	2.75	11.25
Maria	8.61	7.06
Tina	8.61	9.72
Brian	5.29	2.85
Thomas	2.05	6.67
Seth	15.69	17.88
Liam	3.37	5.45

    a Calculate the range for the average number of texts sent on a weekday.

    b Calculate the mean average number of texts sent on a weekday.

    c Calculate the range for the average number of texts sent on a day at the weekend.

    d Calculate the mean average number of texts sent on a day at the weekend.

4 Ella's class also looked at the number of texts sent by boys and girls each day.
Choose appropriate statistics from the table and write a paragraph to compare the number of texts sent by the boys and the girls in Ella's class.

	Number of texts sent each day by:	
	Boys	Girls
mean	7.06	8.90
median	6	10
mode	6	9
range	24	24

15.5 Data in tables and diagrams

1 Copy and complete the following.

a $\frac{1}{2} = \frac{\square}{6}$ b $\frac{2}{3} = \frac{4}{\square}$ c $\frac{4}{\square} = \frac{16}{20}$ d $\frac{\square}{7} = \frac{18}{42}$

2 This two-way table shows the number of boys and girls in a class that are right-handed or left-handed.

	Right-handed	Left-handed	Total
Boys	9	4	
Girls	15	2	
Total			

a Copy and complete the two-way table.

b How many girls are there in the class?

c How many left-handed pupils are there in the class?

d How many pupils are there in the class altogether?

3 This two-way table shows the number of different boxes of cereal in a shop.

	500 g	750 g	1 kg	Total
Cornflakes	12	15		33
Crisped rice	10		5	23
Wheat flakes	4	13		
Total			18	

a Copy and complete the two-way table.

b How many 500 g boxes of cereal are there?

c How many boxes of wheat flakes are there?

d How many boxes of cereal are there in the shop altogether?

4 This stem-and-leaf diagram shows the time taken for pupils in a class to complete a puzzle.

```
1 | 3  4  4  6  6  7  8  9
2 | 0  0  1  1  1  4  6  7  8  9
3 | 1  2  3  3  5  5  7  8  9
```

Key: 1|3 represents 13 seconds.

a How many pupils completed the puzzle in 33 seconds?

b What is the longest time taken to complete the puzzle?

c What is the modal time taken to complete the puzzle?

d What is the range in times taken to complete the puzzle?

e How many pupils are in the class?

5 Dafydd grows leeks. He measures the lengths of 15 of his leeks. Here are his results.

28 cm	31 cm	32 cm	29 cm	35 cm
31 cm	41 cm	26 cm	40 cm	29 cm
28 cm	30 cm	32 cm	27 cm	32 cm

a Draw a stem-and-leaf diagram to show this information.

b What is the modal length of leek?

c What is the median length of leek?

d What is the range in the lengths of the leeks?

Need some help? Look at Section 15.6 on the CD.

15.6 Scatter graphs

1 Write down whether **A**, **B** or **C** is the correct answer to each of these.

   a 0.9 is equivalent to   **A** 0.9%   **B** 9%   **C** 90%

   b $\frac{1}{4}$ is equivalent to   **A** 4%   **B** 25%   **C** 40%

   c 2% is equivalent to   **A** 0.2   **B** 0.02   **C** 0.002

   d $\frac{7}{10}$ is equivalent to   **A** 0.7   **B** 0.07   **C** 0.007

2 This scatter graph shows the height and mass of 15 year-7 boys.

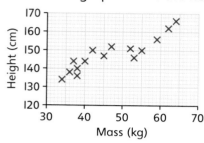

   a What type of correlation does this scatter graph show?

   b What is the mass of the heaviest boy?

   c What is the height of the shortest boy?

   d Alex weighs 50 kg. Estimate his height.

3 This scatter graph shows the age and value of 15 cars of the same make and model.

   a What type of correlation does this scatter graph show?

   b What is the value of the car when it is brand new?

   c What is the value of a two year old car?

   d Sandra has a car that is $3\frac{1}{2}$ years old. Estimate the value of the car.

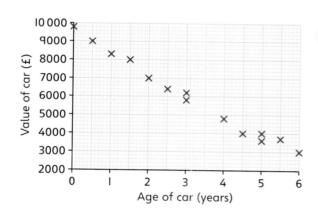

4 Here is some data on the income and shoe size of 10 adults.

Shoe size	3	5	5	3	7
Income (£)	17 000	12 000	18 000	14 000	11 000
Shoe size	8	9	8	9	11
Income (£)	19 000	17 000	13 000	11 000	15 000

   a Plot this data on a scatter diagram.

   b What type of correlation does your scatter graph show?

15.7 Probability revisited

1 Write these measurements in order of size starting with the smallest.

10 m   40 mm   55 cm   0.7 m   670 mm   0.05 km   150 m

2 Select the most appropriate word from the cloud for the likelihood of these events occurring.

a Flipping a coin and getting a tail.

b Throwing a six-sided dice and getting a 0.

c Throwing a six-sided dice and getting a 1.

d Throwing a six-sided dice and getting a number less than 7.

likely   unlikely   certain   evens   impossible

3 Here is a probability scale and a pack of number cards.

Impossible   Unlikely   Evens   Likely   Certain

2   7   5   7

3   2   11   5

a Copy the probability scale into your book.

b Mark these probabilities on the scale, using a cross, and label them with the appropriate letter.
A card is chosen at random from the pack. What is the probability that it is

A an odd number?   **B** the number 5?

C a number greater than 12?   **D** a prime number?

4 Ambika has this bag of coloured counters.
She takes one counter at random from the bag.

a What is the probability that the counter she takes is

  i red?   **ii** yellow?   **iii** blue?

  iv pink?   **v** not orange?   **vi** grey?

b Which of these outcomes are equally likely?

5 Greg has 20 DVDs. 15 of the DVDs are 'Action and Adventure' films.
Greg chooses a DVD at random. What is the probability that

a the DVD is an 'Action and Adventure' film?

b the DVD is **not** an 'Action and Adventure' film?

6 The probability of winning a prize in a raffle is 1%.
What is the probability of **not** winning a prize?

7 List all the outcomes of the following events.

  a Flipping a coin   **b** Rolling a normal dice

  c Taking a card from this pack   **d** Spinning this spinner

3   2   4   8   7   4   3

15.8 Listing outcomes

1 The yellow cards are mixed numbers. The pink cards are improper fractions.
Match each yellow card with its correct pink card.

$1\frac{1}{3}$ $3\frac{1}{5}$ $2\frac{2}{3}$ $2\frac{2}{5}$ $1\frac{2}{3}$ $2\frac{4}{5}$

$\frac{8}{3}$ $\frac{5}{3}$ $\frac{14}{5}$ $\frac{4}{3}$ $\frac{12}{5}$ $\frac{16}{5}$

2 For her coffee break, Lynn has either a cappuccino or mocha coffee.
She also has either a flapjack or biscuit. Copy and complete this table to show all the possible outcomes for Lynn's coffee break.

	Flapjack (F)	Biscuit (B)
Cappuccino (C)	C,F	
Mocha (M)		

5a

3 For lunch, Ahmed has either a sandwich or a baguette. He has either an egg filling or a cheese filling. Copy and complete this table to show all the possible outcomes for Ahmed's lunch.

	Egg (E)	Cheese (C)
Sandwich (S)	S, E	
Baguette (B)		

5a

4 Here is a dice and a coloured spinner. The dice has only the numbers 1, 2 and 3 on it.
Holly rolls the dice and spins the spinner.
Copy and complete this table of possible outcomes.

	1	2	3
Yellow	Y,1		
Blue		B,2	
Red			

6c

5 Here are two spinners.
Rico spins the two spinners and adds together the numbers on the spinners.

a Copy and complete the sample space diagram.

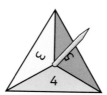
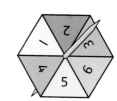

+	1	2	3	4	5	6
3	4	5	6			
4	5					
5						

b Find the probability that Rico scores

    i 4   **ii** 7   **iii** 8   **iv** 10

6a

Play any game on the LiveText CD.

16.1 Powers and roots

1 Copy and complete this money pyramid. Each brick is the sum of the two bricks below it.

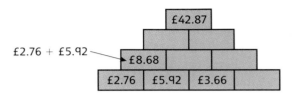

£2.76 + £5.92 ⟶ £8.68

£42.87	
£8.68		
£2.76	£5.92	£3.66

2 Between which two whole numbers do these square roots lie?

   a $\sqrt{14}$ **b** $\sqrt{40}$ **c** $\sqrt{99}$

3 Work these out without using a calculator.

   a $8^2 + 6^2 + 4^2 + 2^2 - 10^2$ **b** $(8 + 6 + 4 + 2 - 10)^2$

4 A box in the shape of a cube can be filled with one tonne of pure water.
Each side of the box measures 100 cm.
What is the volume of the box in cm³?

5 Write down the value of

   a 5^3 **b** $\sqrt[3]{27}$ **c** 10^3 **d** $\sqrt[3]{1}$

6 Work these out without using a calculator.

   a $\left(\sqrt[3]{125}\right)^2$ **b** $\left(\sqrt{25}\right)^3$ **c** $\sqrt{(5^2 \times 2^2)}$ **a** $\left(\sqrt[3]{27}\right)^3$

7 **a** Look at these squares. Each one is twice the length and width of the previous one.

1 cm   2 cm   4 cm

   i How many red squares will fit into the blue square?
   ii How many red squares will fit into the yellow square?

  b Look at these cubes. Each one is twice the length, width and height of the previous one.

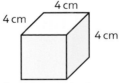

   i How many red cubes will fit into the blue cube?
   ii How many red cubes will fit into the yellow cube?

8 Write in words: **a** 4.7×10^2 **b** 1.35×10^7

5a

6c

6c

6c

6a

6a

6a

16.2 Powers and roots on a calculator

1 On each side of the shape, the numbers in the two circles multiply together to give the number in the square. Copy and complete these.

a

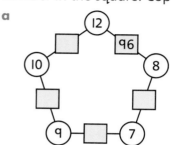

b

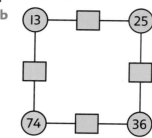

2 Copy and complete this number chain. When you meet a letter (A, B and so on) write down the value of the letter. The chain has been started for you.

$\sqrt{81} = 9$
$\sqrt{9} = 3$
$3 + 13 = 16$
$\sqrt{16} = A$
$A^3 = B$
$\sqrt{B} = C$
$C + 2 = D$
$D^2 = E$
$E + 44 = F$
$\sqrt{F} = G$

3 Here is a shape made from square tiles.
Each square has an area of 81 cm².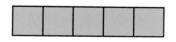
What is the perimeter of the shape?

4 Use your square root key to help you find which two consecutive whole numbers have a product of 22 952.

5 Billy is using wooden blocks to learn to spell.
Each block is a cube with a volume of 64 cm³.
Work out the area of the five faces that spell 'cubes'.

6 Work these out on your calculator.
  a $5 \times \left(\sqrt[3]{216} - 3 \right)$ b $(3^3 - 3^2 - 3)^2$ c $\sqrt{\left(\sqrt{64} - \sqrt[3]{64} \right)}$

7 One of the blocks of stone in the Great Pyramid in Egypt has a volume of 17.576 m³.
The block of stone is a cube.
Use your calculator to work out the height of the cube.

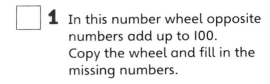
16.3 Multiples, factors and primes

1 In this number wheel opposite numbers add up to 100.
Copy the wheel and fill in the missing numbers.

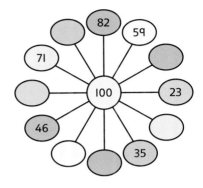

2 Write down the first six multiples of:

   a 4   **b** 5   **c** 6   **d** 7

3 Write down all the factors of:

   a 9   **b** 15   **c** 20   **d** 36

4 Write down the numbers from the cloud that are prime numbers.

5 Use your calculator to help you work out whether 667 is a prime number.

6 Use your answer to question 2 to find the lowest common multiple (LCM) of:

   a 4 and 5   **b** 4 and 6   **c** 5 and 6

7 Use your answers to question 3 to find the highest common factor (HCF) of:

   a 9 and 15   **b** 9 and 36   **c** 20 and 36

8 A concert organiser has 1200 seats to arrange.
The rows of seats **must** be the same length.
There can be a **maximum** of 20 rows.

   a List the different ways the organiser can arrange the seats,
     e.g. 20 rows with 60 seats in each row as 20 × 60 = 1200

   b Which arrangement do you think is the most practical and why?

16.4 LCM, HCF and prime factors

1 a Put these temperatures in order, starting with the coldest.

5°C −4°C −7°C 9°C −1°C 3°C 0°C

b The temperature at midnight is −3°C.
By midday the temperature has gone up by 9°C.
What is the temperature at midday?

c The temperature in a fridge is 4°C.
The temperature in a freezer is −18°C.
How many degrees colder is the freezer?

2 a Find the lowest common multiple of 18 and 12.
b Find the highest common factor of 18 and 12.

5a

3 Alice and Joe are playing the drums.
Alice hits her snare drum every 10 beats.
Joe hits his bass drum every 12 beats.
They start hitting their drums at the same time.
After how many beats will they hit their drums
again at the same time?

5a

4 Beth has some friends round for lunch.
She has 18 vegetable samosas and 24 onion bhajias
to share equally between them (not including herself).

a How many friends could she have round for lunch?
b What is the most number of friends she could have round for lunch?

5a

5 a Find the lowest common multiple of 2, 5 and 8.
b Find the highest common factor of 18, 30 and 48.

6c

6 Copy and complete this factor tree to find the prime factor decomposition of 300.

6b

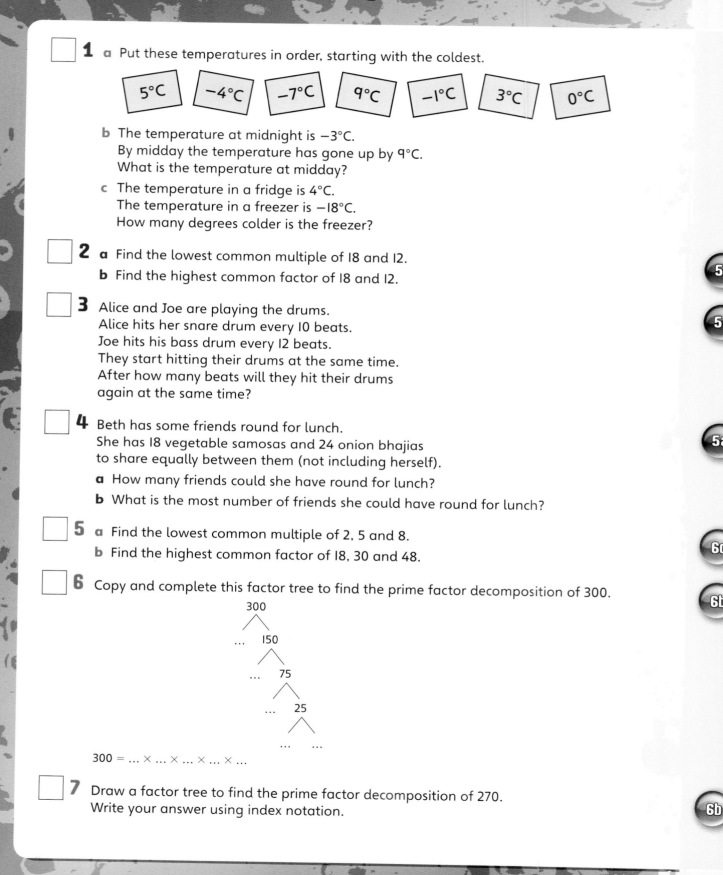

```
          300
          /  \
        ...   150
              /  \
            ...   75
                  /  \
                ...   25
                      /  \
                    ...   ...
```

300 = ... × ... × ... × ... × ...

7 Draw a factor tree to find the prime factor decomposition of 270.
Write your answer using index notation.

6b

16.5 Solving fraction problems

1 Copy and complete these multiplications using any method.

    a 468 × 2   **b** 396 × 7   **c** 382 × 4   **d** 859 × 5

2 Tao cuts a 500 g block of butter into 4 equal pieces.
How much does each piece of butter weigh?

3 **a** Work out the answers to the questions on these cards.

A	B	C	D
$\frac{3}{10}$ of 340 kg	two thirds of 135 kg	180 kg × $\frac{5}{9}$	one tenth of 950 kg

    b Write the answers in order of size starting with the lightest.

4 Write the mass shown on these cards in order of size starting with the lightest.

A	B	C
$\frac{2}{3}$ kg	0.65 kg	$\frac{3}{5}$ kg

5 Work out $\frac{2}{3} + \frac{2}{15} - \frac{2}{5}$

6 Work out $18 \div \frac{3}{5}$

7 Joanne, Gareth and Clarence take part in a 12-metre charity egg race.
Joanne gets 36% of the distance before dropping her egg.

Gareth gets $\frac{2}{5}$ of the distance before dropping his egg.

Clarence gets 0.45 of the distance before dropping his egg.
Who got closest to the finish line before dropping their egg?

5b

5b

5a

6c

6b

6a

Need some help? Look at Section 16.6 on the CD.

16.6 Calculations in problem solving

1 a Which of the numbers on the cards below are prime numbers?

25 I   11 U   19 T   7 C   13 L   23 E   5 L   9 R   17 A

12 S   21 P   3 A   1 M   2 C   18 J

b Write down the cards with prime numbers on, in order of size starting with the smallest. What word have you written?

2 Aidan, Mandek and George want to buy a stunt kite that costs £19.99.
Aidan has £5.12, Mandek has £9.80 and George has £3.05

a Approximately how much do they have altogether?

b Approximately how much more do they need to buy the kite?

c Use a written method to work out **exactly** how much more money they need.

3 Write **true** or **false** for each of these.
Use an approximate calculation to help you decide.

a 12 lots of 52p ≈ £4

b 31.6 × 4.9 ≈ 150

c $96\frac{1}{4} \div 9\frac{4}{5} \approx 7$

d £974 282 shared between 19 people is about £50 000 each.

4 Elisa works out that last year she was given a total of £286 pocket money.
She uses her calculator to work out how much, on average, she was given each week.

Her calculator shows   5.5

Elisa says 'I was given five pounds and five pence pocket money each week'.
What mistake has Elisa made?

5 These are the shoe sizes of six girls.
3, 5, 4, 4, 4, 7
Work out the mean shoe size.

6 a Estimate the answer to 156 × 24 in three different ways.

b Work out the answer to 156 × 24 on your calculator.

c Which of your three estimates in part **a** gives the most accurate answer?

7 Abu works out the mean height of four of his friends.
Their heights are 1 m 36cm, 1.62 m, $1\frac{1}{2}$ m and 152 cm.
Abu gets an answer of 39.12 m.

a What do you think Abu has done wrong?

b Work out the correct answer.
Give your answer in: **i** metres   **ii** centimetres

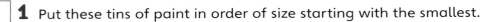

16.7 Fractions on a calculator

1 Put these tins of paint in order of size starting with the smallest.

55 cl   0.72 l   100 cl   0.6 l   850 ml   400 ml

2 Write the numbers shown on the calculator displays as fractions.

a [3.3333333333333]   b [2.6666666666667]

c [6.1666666666667]   d [0.8888888888889]

3 Use your calculator to work these out.

a $\frac{2}{5} + \frac{4}{7}$ b $\frac{7}{10} - \frac{6}{9} + \frac{5}{8}$ c $\frac{2}{5} \times \left(\frac{5}{6} + \frac{5}{8}\right)$ d $\left(\frac{7}{10} - \frac{6}{11}\right) \times \left(\frac{1}{2} - \frac{3}{17}\right)$

4 a Find $\frac{1}{3} + \frac{1}{4} + \frac{1}{5}$

b What fraction must be added to your answer to part **a** to give an answer of $\frac{14}{15}$?

5 Use your calculator to work these out.

a $1\frac{5}{6} + 2\frac{7}{9}$ b $20\frac{1}{12} - 6\frac{3}{4}$

6 a Work out the answers to the questions on these cards.

A	B	C
$5 \times 4\frac{3}{4}$	$3\frac{1}{2} \times 7\frac{4}{9}$	$10 \times 2\frac{7}{15}$

b Write the answers in order of size starting with the smallest.

7 The 'Special Extended' DVD of 'The Lord of the Rings' has three discs.

   Disc 1 is 3 hours 18 minutes long
   Disc 2 is 3 hours 34 minutes long
   Disc 3 is 3 hours 56 minutes long

a Write 3 hours and 18 minutes as a mixed number fraction in hours.

b What is the total length of the three discs in hours and minutes?

c Write your answer to part **b** as a mixed number fraction.

16.8 Multiplication and division problems

1 Use the numbers in the cloud to complete these additions.
You can only use each number in the cloud once.

a 14 + 26 = ☐

b ☐ + 43 = 67

c 19 + ☐ = 35

d ☐ + ☐ = 18

e ☐ + ☐ = 50

f ☐ + 31 = ☐

Cloud: 50   7   22   40   16   28   11   24   19

2 Gaynor paid £278.30
for 11 days car hire.

Malcolm paid £363.75
for 15 days car hire.

Who paid the greater daily rate? Use a written method to work it out.

3 Here is a multiplication fact.

$7 \times 36 = 252$

Use this fact to answer these:

a 0.7×36 **b** 7×0.36 **c** 0.7×3.6 **d** 0.7×0.36

4 Here is a multiplication fact.

$0.4 \times 3.8 = 1.52$

Use this fact to answer these:

a 4×0.0038 **b** 40×3.8 **c** 400×38 **d** 0.004×38000

5 Work these out by using multiplication facts that you already know.

a $3 \times 0.02 = $ ____

b $4 \times 0.02 = $ ____

d $6 \times 0.4 = $ ____

d $0.5 \times 0.5 = $ ____

e $0.05 \times 0.05 = $ ____

f ____ $\times 0.09 = 0.018$

g ____ $\times 60000 = 36\ 000$

6 A sheet of A4 paper measures 29.6 cm by 21cm.
Without using a calculator, find the area of a
sheet of A4 paper.

← 29.6 cm →

21 cm

7 A sheet of A5 paper has an area of 310.8 cm².
The length of the sheet of paper is 21 cm.
Use a written method to work out the width
of the sheet of A5 paper.

← 21 cm →

? | Area = 310.8 cm²

Play any game on the LiveText CD.

17.1 Sequences and finding the nth term

1 Use a calculator to work out $(8.6 + 2.9)^2 \div (8.4 - 5.9)$

2 The diagram shows how many pupils can sit at different numbers of tables.

a Draw a picture for four tables and five tables.

b Copy the table and fill in the missing values.

Number of tables	1	2	3	4	5
Number of pupils	3				

3 Look at this pattern of dots.

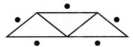

Pattern 1   Pattern 2   Pattern 3

a Draw pattern 4 and pattern 5.

b Copy and complete this table.

c How many blue dots would there be in pattern 12?

Pattern	1	2	3	4	5
Number of blue dots	2				
Number of red dots	1				

4 The diagram shows the number of posts used to make sections of fencing.

a Draw diagrams for four or five sections.

b Copy and complete this table.

Number of sections	1	2	3	4	5
Number of posts	5				

c How many posts will be needed for nine sections?

Explain how you worked out your answer.

5 The terms of a sequence are found by adding together even numbers and taking away the term number.
The **first** term is the **first** even number take away 1: $2 - 1 = 1$
The **second** term is the sum of the first **two** even numbers take away **2**: $2 + 4 - 2 = 4$
The **third** term is the sum of the first **three** even numbers take away **3**: $2 + 4 + 6 - 3 = 9$
Copy and complete this table.

Term number	1	2	3	4	5	6
Term	1	4	9			

6 Find the linear expression (nth term) for these sequences.

a 7, 11, 15, 19, 23, ...   b 23, 19, 15, 11, 7, ...

4b

4a

5b

5a

6c

17.2 More equations

1 a Copy this secret code box.

													T						!
32	6	4	600	60		40	400	24	40		6	4	600	60	240	320	60	60	6	40

b Work the answers to these questions.
Put the letter by each question on the line
above the answer in the secret code box.
For example, the first question is:
$24 \times 10 = 240$, so T goes above 240
in the table.

What is the secret message?

24×10	$= T$
$320 \div 10$	$= L$
6×100	$= R$
$2400 \div 100$	$= M$
$6000 \div 1000$	$= E$
32×10	$= O$
$40 \div 10$	$= A$
$6000 \div 100$	$= N$
4×10	$= S$
$4000 \div 10$	$= U$

2 Solve these equations.

a $6e = 18$ **b** $f + 3 = 25$ **c** $g - 3 = 25$

3 Solve these equations using inverse operations.

a $5h + 3 = 23$ **b** $2i - 5 = 17$ **c** $7 + 3j = 22$

4 Solve these equations using the balancing method.

a $6a + 4 = 16$ **b** $8 + 3b = 35$ **c** $5c - 5 = 5$

5 Solve these equations using the balancing method.

a $7p + 3 = 6p + 11$ **b** $3q + 12 = 5q + 2$ **c** $6r - 4 = 5r + 1$

6 a Write an equation for each of these shapes.

b Solve your equation to find the value of the unknown in each shape.

i

ii
perimeter = 90 cm

iii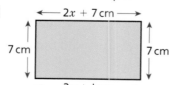

7 Callum thinks of a number, multiplies it by 5 and then subtracts 10.
He then doubles his new number.
His final answer is 70.

a Write an expression for Callum's number.

b Use this to construct and solve an equation to work out the number
Callum first thought of.

17.3 Using formulae

1 Without a calculator work out $(46 \div 2 - 5 \times 3)^2$

2 In a cookery book the instructions for roasting a chicken are:

> Roasting a chicken:
> Allow 40 minutes per kilogram plus an extra 20 minutes.

These instructions can be written as a formula:

Time in minutes = 40 × weight in kg + 20

Work out the roasting time for a chicken weighing

a I kg   **b** 2 kg   **c** $2\frac{1}{2}$ kg.

3 Janet joins a scuba diving club. Each year she pays a £50 membership fee, and then £8 for each dive.
The formula to work out the total cost for the year is:

Total cost (£) = 50 + (8 × number of dives)

Work out the total cost for Janet if she does:

a 5 dives   **b** I0 dives   **c** 20 dives.

4 Mahmoud joins a DVD club. He pays a £I0 membership fee and then £3 for each DVD he hires.
Write a formula connecting C, the total cost in pounds, and n, the number of DVDs hired.

5 The formula for the area of a trapezium is:

$A = \frac{1}{2} \times a \times h + \frac{1}{2} \times b \times h$

Find the area of this trapezium.

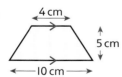

6 A quick way to convert a temperature from °C (degrees Centigrade) to °F (degrees Fahrenheit) is to use the formula:

F = 2C + 30

Work out the temperature in °F when the temperature is − 8°C.

7 **a** Substitute $a = -3$ and $b = 2$ into the side lengths of this shape.
b Is the shape a rectangle or a square?

17.4 Graphs in all four quadrants

1 Write **true** or **false** for each of these.

a 15 is a factor of 30.

b 5 is a factor of 15.

c 12 is a multiple of 24.

d 8 is a multiple of 2.

e 64 ÷ 5 has a remainder of 3.

f 51 ÷ 4 has a remainder of 3.

g 49 is a square number.

h 8 is the square root of 16.

2 Work out the answer to this question using the coordinate grid.
(−5, −5) (−3, −4) (−6, −2)
(−1, −7) (5, 2) (5, 2)
(−3, 8) (−5, −5) (−4, 0)
(3,5) (5,3)
Write your answer in coordinate code.

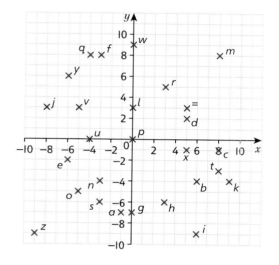

5b

3 a Match each equation to the correct line.

$y = 3x$

$y = 3x + 8$

$y = 3x - 4$

$y = 3x + 3$

b Write down the equation of a line that is parallel to all of the lines in part **a** and that lies between line **C** and line **D**.

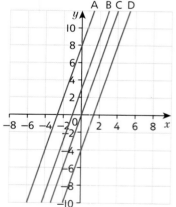

6b

4 a Match each equation to the correct line.

$y = x - 2$

$y = 4x - 2$

$y = 3x - 2$

$y = 8x - 2$

b Write down the equation of a line that also goes through the point (0,−2) and that lies between line **C** and line **D**.

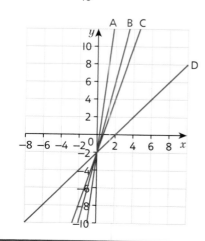

6b

17.5 Winter Olympics

1 The ten judges in a dancing competition awarded a dancer these points:

| 8 | 9 | 9 | 8 | 8 | 10 | 6 | 7 | 10 | 8 |

Work out

a the modal score   **b** the mean score

This is the map for the 'Hunt the Christmas Present' Olympics!

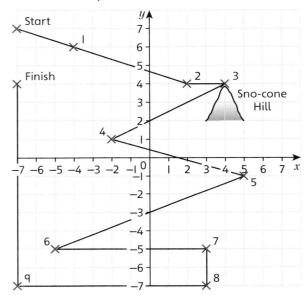

2 Write down the coordinates of all nine presents in order.

3 What is the equation of the line joining presents 8 and 9?

4 What is the equation of the line joining presents 7 and 8?

5 A competitor wants to know how steep it is from present 2 to present 3.
She starts at present 2 and takes readings from her hand-held GPS until she reaches present 3 at the top of Sno-cone Hill.
These are the readings that she takes.

x	0	2	6	12	32
y	0	0.5	1.5	3	8

a Draw a coordinate grid with x-axis from 0 to 40 and y-axis from 0 to 8.
Plot the readings from the table above and draw a straight line through the points.

b She is told that the steepness of the route from present 3 to present 5 has equation $y = \frac{1}{2}x$. On the same axis you used in part **a**, plot the graph of $y = \frac{1}{2}x$.

c Which slope is steeper, the slope from present 2 to 3 or the slope from present 3 to 5?

17.6 Real-life graphs

1 Copy and complete the following.

a $\frac{1}{2} = \frac{\square}{8}$ **b** $\frac{3}{5} = \frac{15}{\square}$ **c** $\frac{5}{\square} = \frac{10}{14}$ **d** $\frac{\square}{9} = \frac{21}{27}$

2 This graph shows the value of British pounds against the value of American dollars.

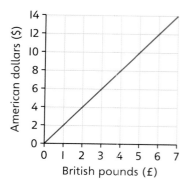

a Use the graph to convert the following into dollars.
   i £3   **ii** £6   **iii** £4.50

b Use the graph to convert the following into pounds.
   i $4   **ii** $10   **iii** $13

3 This graph shows the relationship between miles and kilometres.

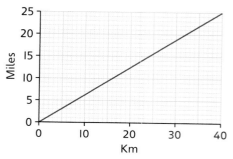

a Use the graph to convert the following into kilometres:
   i 25 miles   **ii** 20 miles   **iii** 10 miles

b Use the graph to convert the following into miles:
   i 24 km   **ii** 8 km   **iii** 15 km

4 Diego plants a tree in his garden. The tag on the tree has this formula for the expected growth of the tree for the first 10 years after planting.

$$H = 0.7 + 0.8 \times Y$$
where: H is the height of the tree in metres
             Y is the number of years since the tree was planted

a Copy and complete this table using the formula.

Y	1	5	10
H			

b Draw a set of axes from 0 to 10.
Label the x-axis 'Years (Y)' and the y-axis 'Height (H metres)'.

c Plot the points from your table and join them with a straight line.

d Use your graph to find out how tall the tree should be three years after planting.

e Use your graph to find out how old the tree should be when it gets to 3.5 m.

17.7 Distance–time graphs

1 Find the missing values from the table below.

	Amount in bank account at start	Amount taken out	Amount in bank account at end
a	£100	£50	
b	£60	£75	
c		£30	−£20
d		£50	−£85

2 This distance-time graph is for a marathon runner.

a Use the distance-time graph to find the distance the runner will go in one hour.

b Use the distance-time graph to find the time it will take the runner to go 10 km.

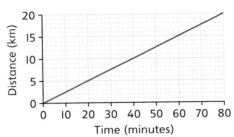

4a

3 Dave goes for a run to get fit. He stops for a rest twice, and gets a taxi home! This graph shows his journey.

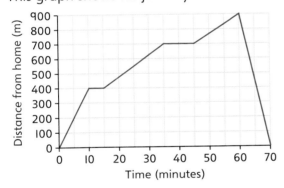

5a

a How far did Dave run before he stopped for the first time?

b For how many minutes did he rest the second time he stopped?

c How far was Dave from his home when he caught the taxi?

d How can you tell from the graph that Dave's journey home was faster than any other part of his journey?

4 Draw a set of axes with the time from 0 to 7 hours on the x-axis and the distance from 0 to 2800 km on the y-axis. Plot a distance-time graph for the following journey:
An aeroplane leaves London and travels 700 km to Frankfurt in 2 hours 15 minutes.
The aeroplane stays in Frankfurt for 1 hour.
It then travels 1900 km to Athens in 3 hours 15 minutes.

6b

17.8 Graphs and direct proportion

1 **a** Find the highest common factor (HCF) of 12 and 18.

b Find the lowest common multiple (LCM) of 12 and 18.

2 Three friends left their homes at the same time to travel the 10 km to school.
One travelled by bus, one by car and one by bicycle.

This is a distance-time graph of their journeys. Which friend travelled

a by bus

b by car

c by bicycle?

Give reasons for your answers.

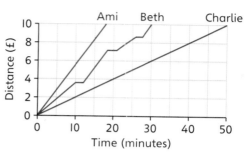

3 This graph shows the yearly drink sales of a shop.

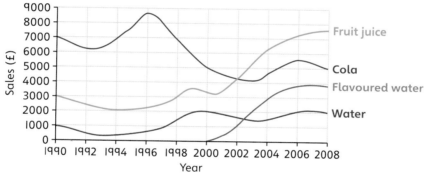

a In which year did the sales of cola reach their peak?

b In which year did fruit juice become more popular than cola?

c In which year did the shop introduce flavoured water?

4 When could we say that the following values are in direct proportion?

a Amount of chocolate bought and the total cost of the chocolate.

b Number of pages in a file and the weight of the file.

c Volume of fruit juice and the number of cartons of fruit juice.

5 Plot these values on a graph to help you decide whether or not the values are in direct proportion. Explain your reasoning.

Units of electricity used	200	400	600	800	1000	1200
Cost (£)	28.50	44.50	60.50	76.50	92.50	108.50

18.1 Constructions

1 Convert these improper fractions to mixed numbers.

   a $\frac{7}{3}$ **b** $\frac{14}{5}$ **c** $\frac{22}{7}$ **d** $\frac{20}{9}$

2 Measure these angles to the nearest degree.

   a   **b**

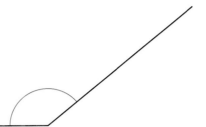

3 Draw these acute angles accurately using a ruler and protractor.

   a 25°   **b** 58°   **c** 87°

4 Work out the value of angles c, d, e, f and g in these diagrams.
Show your calculations and explain how you found each answer.

   a   **b**

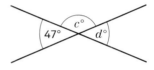

5 Construct these triangles using a ruler and protractor.

   a   **b**

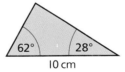
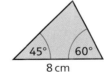

6 Two trees are 80 m apart.
A company lays a pipeline directly between the trees
as shown on the sketch.

   a Use a scale of 1 cm = 10m to draw a diagram of
the position of the two trees.
Join them with a dotted line.

   b Use a ruler and compasses to construct the 80 m perpendicular bisector of the dotted
line to show the route of the pipeline.

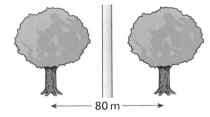

7 At football training, Owen runs around this triangular circuit.

   a Use a ruler and compasses to construct a scale drawing
of the triangular circuit. Use the scale 1 cm = 1m.

   b Owen runs around the circuit four times.
What is the total distance he has run?

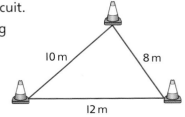

 4a
 5a
 5a
 6c
6a

18.2 Drawing 3-D shapes

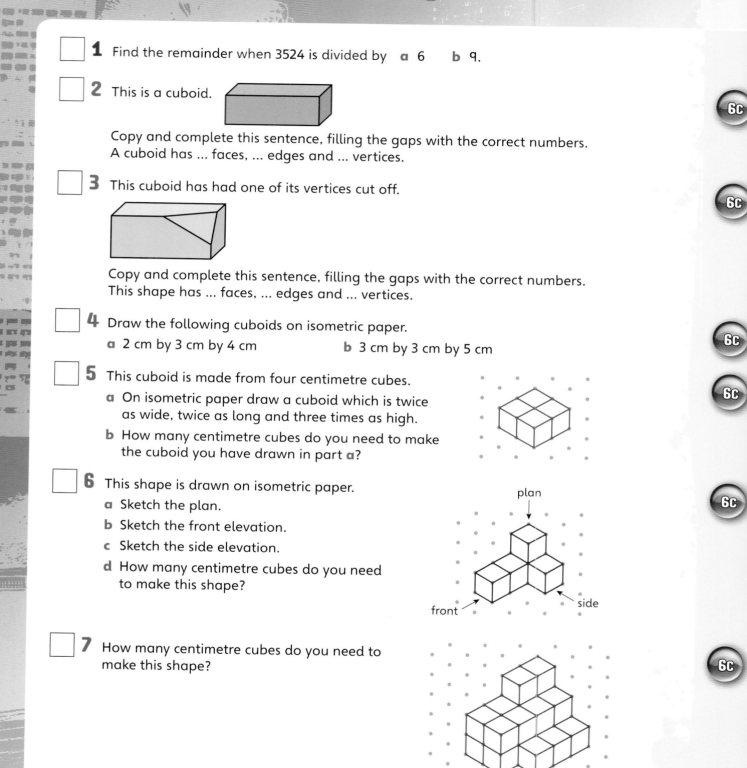

1 Find the remainder when 3524 is divided by **a** 6   **b** 9.

2 This is a cuboid.

Copy and complete this sentence, filling the gaps with the correct numbers.
A cuboid has ... faces, ... edges and ... vertices.

3 This cuboid has had one of its vertices cut off.

Copy and complete this sentence, filling the gaps with the correct numbers.
This shape has ... faces, ... edges and ... vertices.

4 Draw the following cuboids on isometric paper.
   a 2 cm by 3 cm by 4 cm   **b** 3 cm by 3 cm by 5 cm

5 This cuboid is made from four centimetre cubes.
   a On isometric paper draw a cuboid which is twice
      as wide, twice as long and three times as high.
   b How many centimetre cubes do you need to make
      the cuboid you have drawn in part **a**?

6 This shape is drawn on isometric paper.
   a Sketch the plan.
   b Sketch the front elevation.
   c Sketch the side elevation.
   d How many centimetre cubes do you need
      to make this shape?

plan

front   side

7 How many centimetre cubes do you need to
make this shape?

18.3 Nets of cuboids

1 Copy and complete this number pyramid.
Find each missing amount by
adding the two bricks below it.

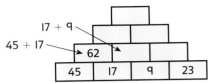
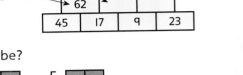
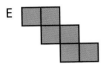

2 Which of the following could be the net of a closed cube?

 A B C D E

3 This is the net of a cuboid.

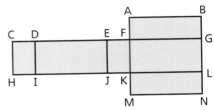

When the net is folded up to make the cuboid, which edge meets with:

a AB   **b** CD   **c** EF   **d** CH?

4 This cuboid is drawn on isometric paper.
The dimensions of the cuboid are
1 cm high by 2 cm wide by 3 cm long.
Accurately construct the net of this cuboid.

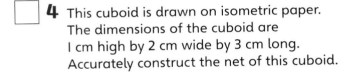

5 a Accurately construct the net of this open cube with sides of
length 2.5 cm.

b Use your net to measure the length of the diagonal on
one of the sides of the cube, shown as a red line on the
diagram.

6 Look at this cube.
Write **true** or **false** for each of these statements.

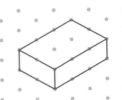

a AB is parallel to DH.

b EG is perpendicular to GH.

c CD, BD and DH all meet at the same point.

d AC is parallel and equal in length to FH.

18.4 More nets

1 a Write down the numbers from the cloud that are prime numbers.

b Write down the numbers from the cloud that are square numbers.

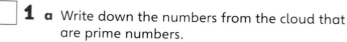

9 29 25 4
35 13 2 5
7 12 1 45 16

c Add together the numbers from the cloud you haven't used in parts **a** and **b**.

d Subtract the total in part **c** from 100.

e Write down the square of your answer from part **d**.

2 Each of these nets can be folded into a 3-D shape.
Write down the name of the 3-D shape that each net makes.

a   **b**    **c**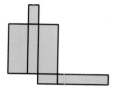

5c

3 This is a tetrahedron   This is a net of the tetrahedron.
(triangular based pyramid).

   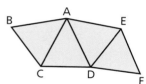

B   A   E
C   D   F

5c

When the net is folded up to make the tetrahedron, which edge meets with:

a AB   **b** CD   **c** EF?

4 Use a ruler and pencil to sketch the nets for each of these shapes.

a   **b**

5b

5 Construct an accurate net for this triangular prism.

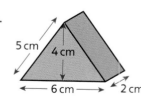

5 cm   4 cm
6 cm   2 cm

5b

18.5 Surface area

1 Copy and complete this number chain. When you meet a letter (A, B and so on) write down the value of the letter. The chain has been started for you.

$\sqrt{16} = 4$　　$\sqrt{4} = 2$　　$2 + 23 = 25$　　$\sqrt{25} = A$　　$A^3 = B$

$B - 25 = C$　　$\sqrt{C} = D$　　$D + 39 = E$　　$\sqrt{E} = F$

2 This diagram shows the net of a closed cube.

   a Find the area of one of the faces of the cube.

   b After the cube is assembled,
      Rhian wants to paint the outside.
      Find the total surface area of paint that Rhian needs.

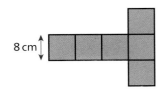

8 cm

3 a Sketch a cuboid with length 8 cm, width 2 cm and height 4 cm.

   b Sketch a net of the cuboid.

   c Write the area of each face on the net.

   d Find the surface area of the cuboid.

4 Calculate the surface area of these cuboids.

a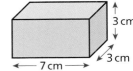

3 cm

3 cm

7 cm

b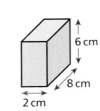

6 cm

8 cm

2 cm

5 This shape is made from two cuboids.
Calculate the surface area of the shape.

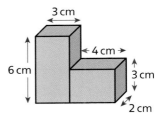

3 cm

4 cm

6 cm

3 cm

2 cm

6 This statue is made from three **identical** cuboids.
Javier has to paint the statue.

   a Calculate the surface area of the statue.

   b Paint comes in five-litre pots.
      One litre will cover 3 m².
      How many pots does Javier need to buy?

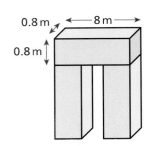

0.8 m　　8 m

0.8 m

18.6 Volume

1 **a** Write down the first five multiples of 8.
   b Write down the first five multiples of 12.
   c What is the lowest common multiple (LCM) of 8 and 12?
   d Write down all the factors of 18.
   e Write down all the factors of 24.
   f What is the highest common factor (HCF) of 18 and 24?

2 What is the volume of a cube with side length 4 cm?

3 Find the volume of these shapes made from centimetre cubes.
   a   **b**

4 This block of marble is in the shape of a cube.
   The cube has a side length of 20 cm.
   It is sawn into four equal sections.
   Find the volume of one of the sections of marble.

5 Find the volume of these cuboids.
   a   **b**

6 The diagram shows a wooden beam.
   a Find the volume of wood in the beam.
   b 20% of the wooden beam is rotten.
      What is the volume of rotten wood in the beam?

7 The stingray tank in an aquarium is a 15 m × 12 m × 80 cm cuboid.
   The tank is one-third full.
   a Find the volume of water in the tank.
   b Water is added at a rate of 1.5 m³ per minute.
      How long will it take to fill the tank so that it is two-thirds full?